Challenging
Calcu-doku
Puzzles

Conceptis Puzzles

STERLING INNOVATION
An imprint of Sterling Publishing Co., Inc.

New York / London
www.sterlingpublishing.com

STERLING, the Sterling logo, STERLING INNOVATION, and the Sterling
Innovation logo are registered trademarks of Sterling Publishing Co., Inc.

2   4   6   8   10   9   7   5   3   1

Published by Sterling Publishing Co., Inc.
387 Park Avenue South, New York, NY 10016
© 2010 by Sterling Publishing Co., Inc.

Distributed in Canada by Sterling Publishing
$^c/_o$ Canadian Manda Group, 165 Dufferin Street
Toronto, Ontario, Canada M6K 3H6
Distributed in the United Kingdom by GMC Distribution Services
Castle Place, 166 High Street, Lewes, East Sussex, England BN7 1XU
Distributed in Australia by Capricorn Link (Australia) Pty. Ltd.
P.O. Box 704, Windsor, NSW 2756, Australia

Printed in China
All rights reserved

Sterling ISBN 978-1-4027-7772-1

For information about custom editions, special sales, premium and
corporate purchases, please contact Sterling Special Sales
Department at 800-805-5489 or specialsales@sterlingpublishing.com.

Contents

Introduction

Calcu-Doku in a Nutshell
Calcu-Doku are math and logic puzzles that require placing numbers in a grid according to certain rules. Each puzzle consists of a grid containing blocks surrounded by bold lines. The object is to fill all empty squares so that the numbers 1 to N (where N is the number of rows or columns in the grid) appear exactly once in each row and column. The numbers in each block produce the result of the operation shown in the upper left corner of the block. In Calcu-Doku Numberfest, a number may be used more than once in the same block (but not more than once in each row or column).

Calcu-Doku puzzles are available in different variants. Single Operation Calcu-Doku uses one math operation, which is either addition or multiplication. Similarly, Dual Operation Calcu-Doku uses two math operations (either addition and subtraction or multiplication and division), while Quad Operation Calcu-Doku uses four math operations (addition, subtraction, multiplication, and division) all at the same time. The math operation used in each block is shown in its upper left corner (except for Single Operation Calcu-Doku, where the operation used applies to every block and is shown above the grid).

Calcu-Doku Techniques
Let's look at a sample puzzle to learn some basic techniques of Calcu-Doku.

Starting With the Givens
Some Calcu-Doku puzzles, especially easy ones, contain blocks consisting of a single square. These are actually given clues and the number to be placed is simply the number in the upper left corner of the single square block, regardless of which math operations are shown above the grid. We can therefore place 2 in the example below.

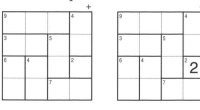

Unique Block Technique

As with kakuro and Sum Sudoku, Calcu-Doku puzzles often have situations where only a single combination of numbers can fit in a block. These situations are useful when starting to solve a puzzle, especially if they appear in straight blocks. Here is one way of using this technique.

In the right column of the Single Operation Calcu-Doku puzzle on the previous page we see a block of two squares with the sum 4. Calcu-Doku rules don't allow the same number to appear more than once in a row or a column, so it couldn't be 2 + 2, even if a 2 weren't already placed in that column. This means the only combination to satisfy the requirement is 1 + 3 or 3 + 1 (though we don't know which one goes where yet). This means that the bottom square in the right column can't be a 1, a 2, or a 3. It must be a 4. Therefore, the number to the left of the 4 must be 7 − 4 = 3.

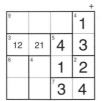

Hidden Single Technique

Look at the block that adds up to 3. It must contain a 1 + 2 or a 2 + 1. Knowing that, the box to its right (which contains a small 5) can be filled in using the Hidden Single Technique. This is when there is only one square in a row, column, or block where a certain number can go; in this case there's only one place a 4 can go in the second row. A 1 can then be placed below (5 − 4 = 1).

Grid Remainder Technique

At this point we can use a different technique that uses the fact that each row and column adds up to the same number (in this case, 10). You see how the long block in the top row adds up to 9? That means that the square in the upper-right corner must be a 1 (10 − 9). We can place a 3 in the box below the 1 as well.

5

Look at the block that adds up to 6. It can't be a 3 + 3, so it must be 2 + 4 or 4 + 2. Since there's already a 4 in the bottom row, we can tell which goes where.

9			4 1
3 12	21	5 4	3
6 4	4	1	2 2
2		7 3	4

Now it's just a matter of filling in the missing digit in each of the bottom two rows, filling in the block that adds up to 3, and filling in the three missing digits in the top row. Does the big block add up to 9? Of course, the answer is yes.

The completed sample should look like this:

9 3	4	2	4 1
3 1	2	5 4	3
6 4	4 3	1	2 2
2	1	7 3	4

Similar techniques can be used in the multiplication and division puzzles. Note that subtraction and division are always in blocks made up of two squares, with the lower number subtracted from the higher number, or the higher number divided by the lower number. Within each size of puzzle the difficulty increases, so it might be a good idea to have a calculator handy for the last few puzzles in each section. Be sure to visit Conceptis Puzzles online at www.conceptispuzzles.com for more advanced tips and tricks.

1 +

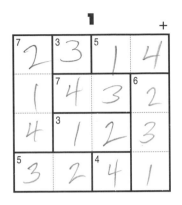

⁷2	³3	⁵1	4
1	⁷4	3	⁶2
4	³1	2	3
⁵3	2	⁴4	1

2 +

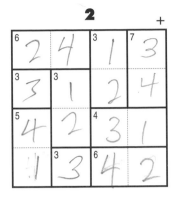

⁶2	4	³1	⁷3
³3	³1	2	4
⁵4	2	⁴3	1
1	³3	⁶4	2

3 +

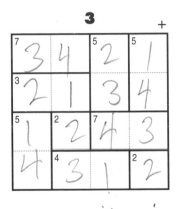

⁷3	4	⁵2	⁵1
³2	1	3	4
⁵1	²2	⁷4	3
4	⁴3	1	²2

4 +

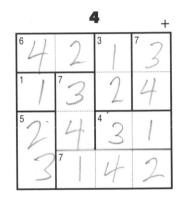

⁶4	2	³1	⁷3
¹1	⁷3	2	4
⁵2	4	⁴3	1
3	⁷1	4	2

5 +

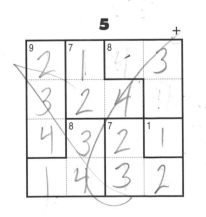

⁹2	⁷1	⁸4	3
3	2	4	
4	⁸3	⁷2	1
1	4	3	2

6 +

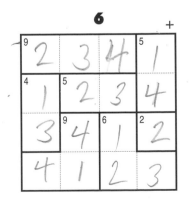

⁹2	3	4	⁵1
⁴1	⁵2	3	4
3	⁹4	⁶1	²2
4	1	2	3

7 +

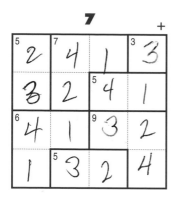

8 +

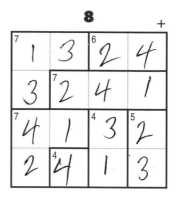

9 +

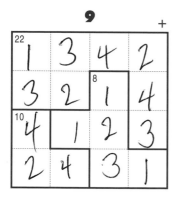

10 +

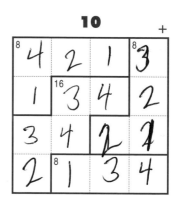

11 +

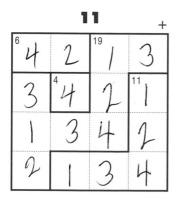

12 +

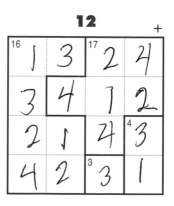

13 +

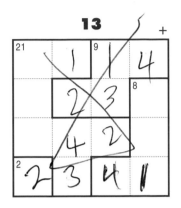

14 ×

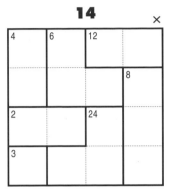

15 ×

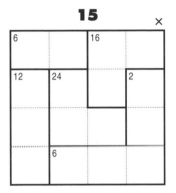

16 ×

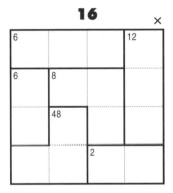

17 ×

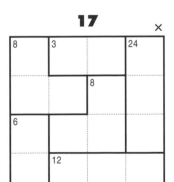

18 ×

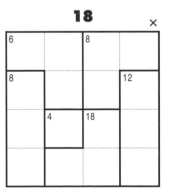

19

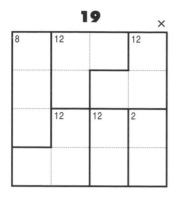

20

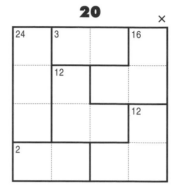

21

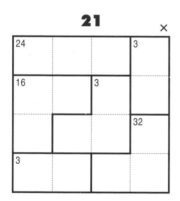

22

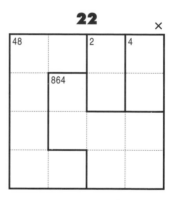

23

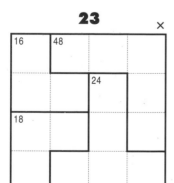

24

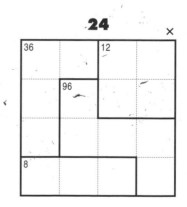

25 ×

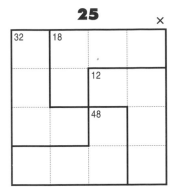

26 ×

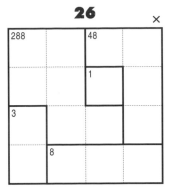

27 + −

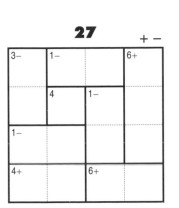

28 + −

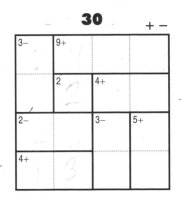

29 + −

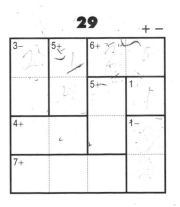

30 + −

31

+ −

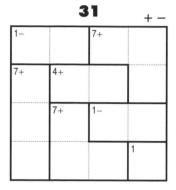

32

+ −

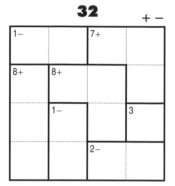

33

+ −

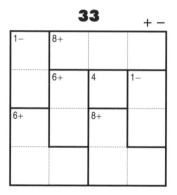

34

+ −

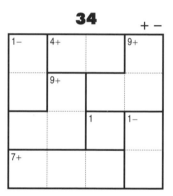

35

+ −

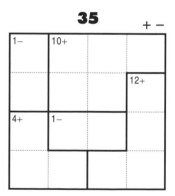

36

+ −

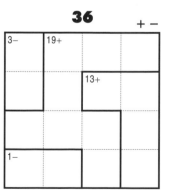

37

+ −

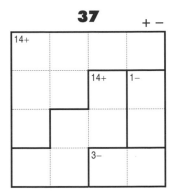

38

+ −

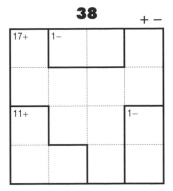

39

+ −

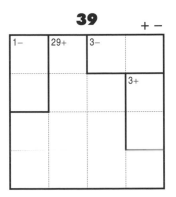

40

× ÷

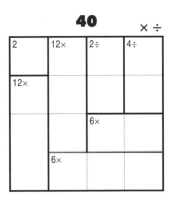

41

× ÷

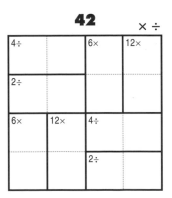

42

× ÷

13

43

× ÷

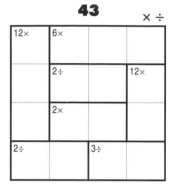

44

× ÷

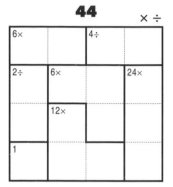

45

× ÷

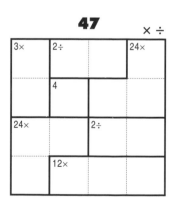

46

× ÷

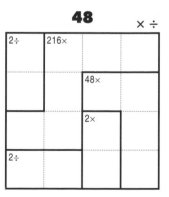

47

× ÷

48

× ÷

14

49
× ÷

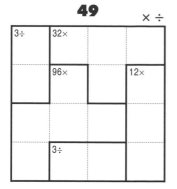

3÷	32×		
	96×		12×
	3÷		

50
× ÷

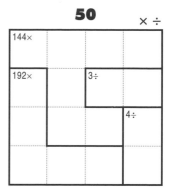

144×			
192×		3÷	
			4÷

51
× ÷

6×	12×		4÷
	576×		
		2÷	

52
× ÷

96×	2÷		72×
2÷		12×	

53
+ − × ÷

3÷	4	2×	
	2−		9+
12×		4+	
3+			

54
+ − × ÷

1−		4÷	
8+	2	12×	5+
	4×		
		2÷	

15

55

+ − × ÷

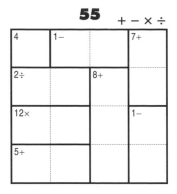

56

+ − × ÷

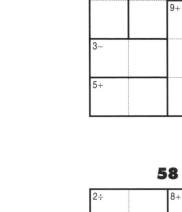

57

+ − × ÷

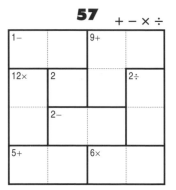

58

+ − × ÷

59

+ − × ÷

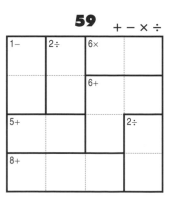

60

+ − × ÷

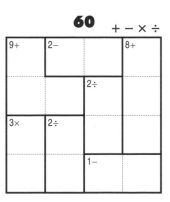

61 + − × ÷

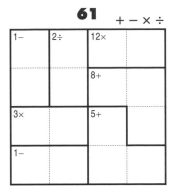

62 + − × ÷

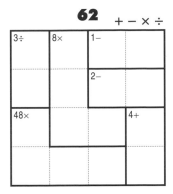

63 + − × ÷

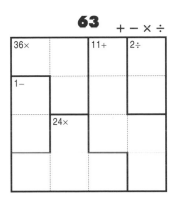

64 + − × ÷

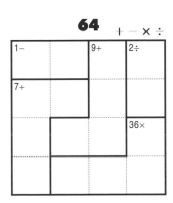

65 + − × ÷

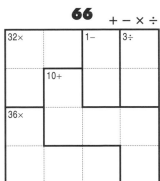

66 + − × ÷

17

67

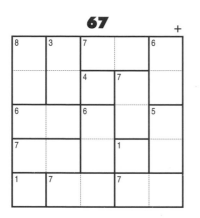

68

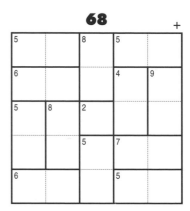

69

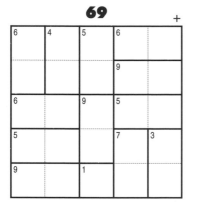

70

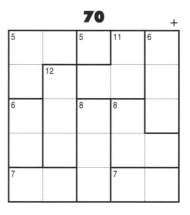

71

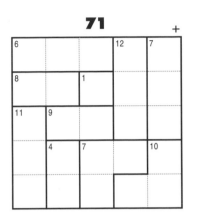

72

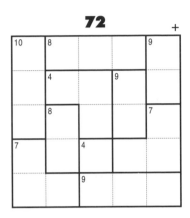

73

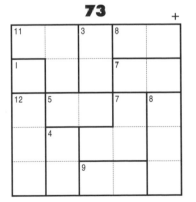

74

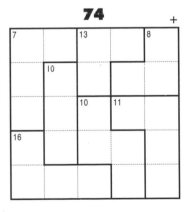

19

75

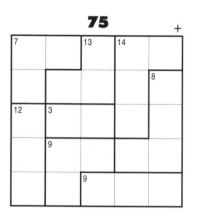

76

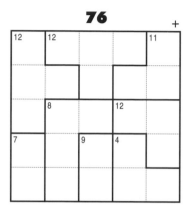

77

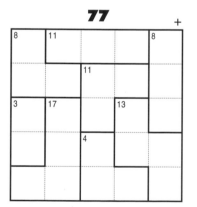

78

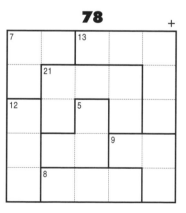

20

79 +

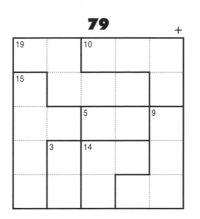

19		10		
15				
		5		9
	3	14		

80 +

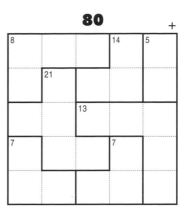

8			14	5
		21		
			13	
7			7	

81 +

8	21		6	
5	11			17
7				

82 +

10		3		8
7		11		
	25		11	

21

83 +

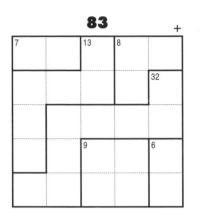

84 +

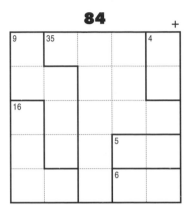

85 ×

2	12	20		5
		6		
5		2	12	6
20		5		
6			4	

86 ×

15		10	4	
3	8		6	
		20		1
2		3	12	10
20				

87 ×

3	20	2	4	
		15	6	
5			2	20
8	12			
	2		15	

88 ×

20			6	2
40				12
12	15			
	2	10		
		60		

89 ×

3	40			6
40			5	
20	12	2		
			12	
		30		

90 ×

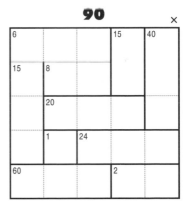

6			15	40
15	8			
		20		
		1	24	
60			2	

91

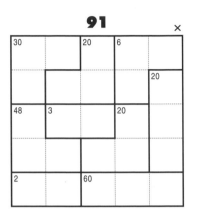

92

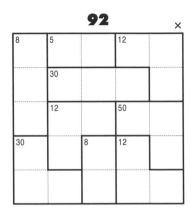

93

×

20		12	15	
20				
	12	30		2
			80	
6				

94

×

20	3		60	6
		40		
12				
		8	20	
15				

95 ×

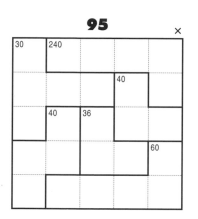

96 ×

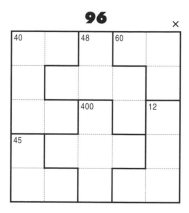

97 ×

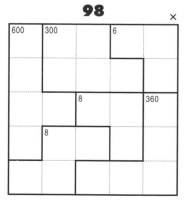

98 ×

99

×

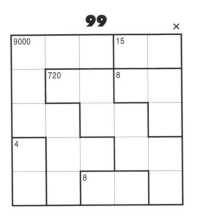

9000			15	
	720		8	
4				
		8		

100

×

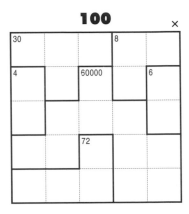

30			8	
4		60000		6
		72		

101

×

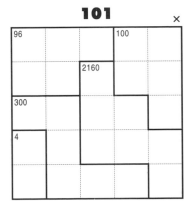

96			100	
		2160		
300				
4				

102

+ −

7+		5+	4−	
3−			3−	
4−	1−		1−	5+
	3+			
4+		2−		5

103

+ −

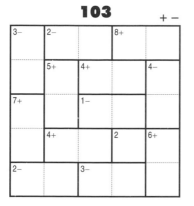

104

+ −

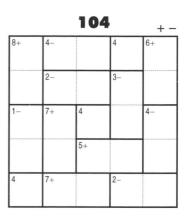

105

+ −

5+	12+	8+	
		1−	4−
1−		2−	
	9+		5+
7+		5	

106

+ −

1−	4−	7+	
		8+	3−
3+		12+	6+
9+			
5	3−		

27

107 + −

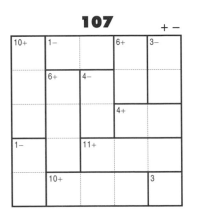

108 + −

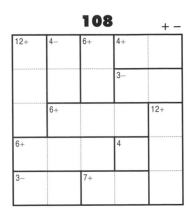

109 + −

110 + −

28

111
+ −

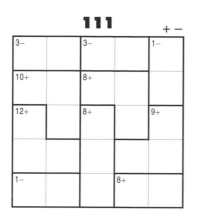

3−		3−		1−
10+		8+		
12+		8+		9+
1−		8+		

112
+ −

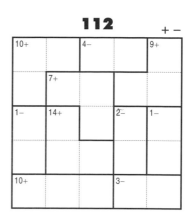

10+		4−		9+
	7+			
1−	14+		2−	1−
10+			3−	

113
+ −

15+	3−		1−	
			14+	
1−		7+		
	19+			1−

114
+ −

14+		10+		
	2−			19+
3+		18+	2−	
	1−			

29

115

116

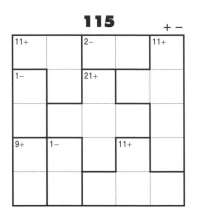

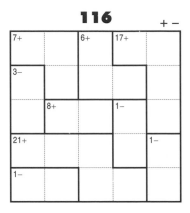

117

118

119

$+ \, -$

1−	6+	31+		
			11+	2−
10+				
	2−		2−	

120

$\times \div$

2	5÷	12×		2÷
15×		20×		
	4÷		10×	12×
2÷		6×		
12×			5÷	

121

$\times \div$

6×	3÷		4÷	20×
	10×			
5÷	8×	20×		3÷
		15×	2	
4÷			6×	

122

$\times \div$

20×		8×	3÷	
10×			5÷	6×
4	3÷			
3÷	6×	4÷		20×
		10×		

123　　× ÷

15×	60×			10×
	8×			
	2÷		3÷	4÷
2÷	6×	5		
	15×			

124　　× ÷

4÷	24×			15×
	6×		15×	
30×	2÷	20×		
				4
	5÷		2÷	

125　　× ÷

15×		2÷	4÷	2
24×	5÷			12×
		15×		
	10×			
4÷		30×		

126　　× ÷

2÷		75×		4×
18×			20×	
5÷		2÷		
	20×		12×	
		3÷		

32

127   × ÷

60×		2÷		5÷
	4÷	18×		
2÷			10×	
	30×	20×		12×

128   × ÷

5÷	2÷		15×	
		4÷	30×	
12×				2÷
12×	75×		16×	

129   × ÷

15×		2÷	2÷	
30×			12×	
		20×		
4÷	2÷		30×	15×

130   × ÷

90×			4×	
	300×	2÷		12×
2÷			75×	
	4÷			

131

× ÷

2÷	3÷		500×	
	2÷			3÷
15×		240×		
			24×	

132

× ÷

2÷	3÷	300×		
		6×	4×	
60×				
	300×			
	2÷			

133

× ÷

2÷		240×		6×
			300×	
2÷				
	60×	12×	5÷	

134

× ÷

2÷		240×		
18000×	120×			
	3÷			2÷

135

× ÷

5	2÷	5760×	2÷	
				900×
12×				
		5÷		

136

× ÷

2÷		300×		
2880×				
60×				
		10×		
		3÷		2

137

+ − × ÷

5+		20×	6+	
8×	2−		3−	15×
		2÷		
9+			1−	
5÷		3	2÷	

138

+ − × ÷

2−	6×		3−	
	9+		3÷	2÷
2÷		5		
8×	5+		3−	8+
	3×			

139

+ − × ÷

2÷	2−		4×	
	3+		1−	15×
6+	1−			
	5+	4÷	8×	
3			5÷	

140

+ − × ÷

2÷	11+	12×	6×	
			5÷	
3		4−		8+
12+			2−	
8+				

141

+ − × ÷

3−		15×	2÷	2−
6+	2			
	12+	9+		
6×		10+		
		5÷		2

142

+ − × ÷

3−		4÷	2÷	10+
3×				
7+	9+			
	1−	10×		4
		9+		

143

+ − × ÷

45×		15+	2÷
2÷			1−
	20×	9×	
	14+		
1−			

144

+ − × ÷

45×		20×	2÷
	12+		2−
		12+	
20×			
	1−	5÷	

145

+ − × ÷

10+	2÷	12×	
		1−	100×
	1−		
11+		16+	2÷

146

+ − × ÷

48×		6+		2−
	21+			
	7+	2÷		3−
15×				
			2÷	

37

147

$+ - \times \div$

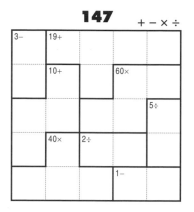

148

$+ - \times \div$

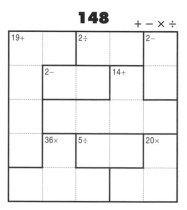

149

$+ - \times \div$

150

$+ - \times \div$

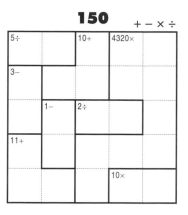

151

+

3		9	5	11	
7	4			4	
	12			9	10
9			12		
8	4			2	
	11			6	

152

+

10			2	7	14
5	10				
	4	11	14		
10	9			9	
		5		8	
			8		

153

+

3	9			9	12
	11		1		
7		11			
13	8	4	13	5	
				7	
	5			8	

154

+

6	6	7	8		
5			10		12
		13			
8			3	11	
8	7				7
	15				

155

+

13		13	6	10	
11	13		15	7	
	2			10	13
	5	8			

156

+

12		8	12		
	10		4		12
9				14	
	10				
		6	13		8
8					

157

+

15	6		7	11	
	12			6	
				11	
12					4
9		9	12		
			12		

158

+

5	8	9			6
		12	12		
16					8
		4	8	6	
11					13
	8				

42

159

+

24		7		20	
7					16
		20		3	
11			18		

160

+

11			15		
12	23				19
		17		10	
	12				
				7	

43

161

16	7			13	
			24		3
5		16		15	
	18				
9					

162

16			4	9	16
	5				
17	3		25		
			8		
17					
			6		

44

163

17	10		18		12
9		31			
			7		
				19	
	3				

164

6		11	14		
	37			8	
12					14
	10				
			4		
10					

45

165

+

```
12          4          10

14       23  24

                13

     26
```

166

+

```
7       32

8               6

            15  10

8                   8

16              16
```

46

167

+

12			10			24
				42		
	8			8		
						7
	15					

168

+

3		13	42		6
10					
	6				5
23		5			
8					
		5			

47

169

+

11	11	42		3	
		6			
20			8		
			9		
9				7	

170

+

24			6		7
	46			11	
			17		
				9	
6					

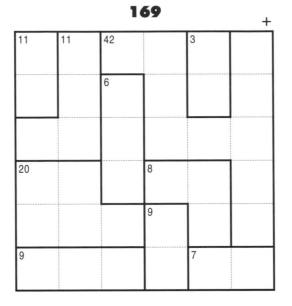

×

30			24		
4		10	90		
36	6		10	12	
	4			8	60
	12				
30			3		

×

30			4	24	
18				12	30
12	20	4	90		
		2		5	
12				3	
	60			4	

173

×

6	24	30			4
		5	12	90	
	6				12
120	30	2			
		4	40		
			18		

174

×

120			12	4	90
1	6				
24	12	20			
		15	120		
			6		
30			24		

175

×

48	4	6	30		
			15		24
	24		20		
45			12		
	30	20	72		

176

×

90			24	24	
24		20			60
			12		
3	5	20			
24			36		
		30			

51

177

×

20	24			60	
		6	18	6	
60				2	
	60		20		36
36					
		40			

178

×

12			72	15	
16	5			48	
		75			48
30		24			
	36		3		
			10		

179

×

120	10		96		
		12		150	36
48					
	18				
		180		120	

180

×

54	60		2		240
				216	
40					
	60				
30			192	30	

181

×

4	96			45	
			20		120
108				144	
	150				
60			24		

182

×

240	144	12			30
	180				12
	150		12		
6			480		

54

183

×

10	4608			15	
		72000			
432					24
			270		

184

×

20		576		1080
18				
	21600			
			4	300
24				

185

×

360			360		
		216			
	21600	7200			
				32	

186

×

6	60		60		
	360				
40		3240	8		
36	10				
	48				

56

187

×

60			72		
4320				180	
		800			
	48				
	60		18		

188

×

180		1200		24	
		24			
				21600	
10	2592				
			2		

189

×

6480				180
	40	1440		
192				144
	75			

190

×

180		18	120	
		60	180	
61440				
18				30

58

+ −

7+		11+	2−	2−	2−
7+	10+				
			6+		
12+	1−	1−		5+	
		12+		2	
	8+			8+	

+ −

5−		4−	12+		
3−			5+		15+
3−		3−		13+	
9+	8+	3+			
		11+			3+
	14+			1	

193

+ −

9+	9+	1−		11+	
		6+	6+		2−
7+			4−		
7+	2−		1−	4−	
	10+			1	9+
1	8+		2−		

194

+ −

11+			9+		4−
11+			4−	8+	
1−		8+			4
4+	9+		8+	5−	
				4−	
15+				1−	

60

195

+ −

4−	2	11+	10+		12+
	11+				
		1−	9+		
3+				1−	2−
16+	2−		8+		
				4−	

196

+ −

15+		9+	3−	7+
	2−			
8+	5+	14+		
			2−	14+
	1−		2−	1−
7+		2		

61

197

+ −

1−	1−		14+		
	12+			6+	
9+	2−	1−			9+
		3	8+	1−	
	4+				
12+				7+	

198

+ −

2−	12+			8+	
	1−		5−		
4−		9+	11+	11+	
7+	5				5−
	9+		1−	10+	

62

199

14+	3−		4−		21+
2−		8+			
	24+			8+	
3−		6+		17+	

200

1−		20+			3−
6	2−			1−	
22+	8+				10+
		7+			
			11+		20+
1−					

201

+ −

18+	5+		11+		8+
			5−		
11+		24+		2−	
			6+		5−
			18+		
3−					

202

+ −

5−		13+		2−	4−
7+			24+		
1−		7+	2−		19+
9+					
	8+			7+	

64

203

+ −

28+			5−		9+
		1−		16+	
		12+			4−
13+					
	1−	1−			
		14+			

204

+ −

11+	15+		47+	1−	
					4−
			5+		
11+					
				13+	
	1−				

65

205

+ −

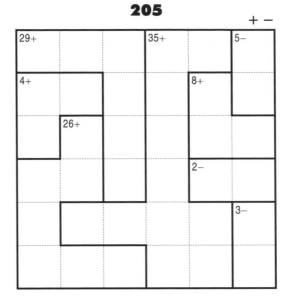

206

+ −

207

+ −

21+			1−	51+	
4+					
	2−				
1−	4−		10+		
	10+				

208

+ −

23+	6+		5−		9+
			11+		
9+				41+	
		1−			
3−				3−	
				1−	

67

209

+ −

8+		40+	3−	1−	15+
	4−				
10+	1−				
18+			4−		
	10+				

210

+ −

13+		43+		12+	
	1−		12+		
			2−		3−
3−					
		1−	20+		
			2−		

68

211

$$\times \div$$

2×		30×	12×	18×	
2÷	6÷			4×	5
		2÷	5		3÷
15×			12×		
30×	12×	6÷		10×	2÷
		3÷			

212

$$\times \div$$

5	15×	2÷	2÷	24×	
12×				2÷	18×
	6÷		15×		
4÷		30×		10×	
12×	2÷		4	3÷	
		2÷		20×	

213

36×			60×	4÷	60×
40×	6×				
	4÷			30×	
	90×				6÷
6×		4÷			
15×			4	3÷	

214

5÷		6÷	24×		
18×	6		40×		
	2÷		20×	3×	
	10×			12×	90×
60×					
2÷		2÷			

215

× ÷

60×		12×		20×	
2÷		3			2÷
	16×	180×		30×	
					8×
90×	3÷		60×		
		2÷			

216

× ÷

2:		54×		100×	
3÷	60×		2÷		
			2÷	6×	6
60×					
20×		12×	90×	24×	

217

× ÷

4÷		2÷		10×	
36×		100×			24×
	30×		18×		
		36×	4		
2÷			20×		
	5÷		36×		

218

× ÷

30×		60×	2÷	12×	
					2÷
30×		120×		2÷	
	12×		9×		40×
2÷				180×	
		1			

219

× ÷

24×		180×			2÷
720×		6÷			
		2÷	360×		30×
90×	4÷				120×

220

× ÷

180×		60×			
		2÷		18×	144×
120×					
2÷			75×		
2÷	4÷				80×
	6÷				

221

2÷	5÷		432×		
	72×		150×		
4÷			2÷		10×
54×					
300×		2÷		72×	

222

48×	6÷		60×		2÷
		180×			
	120×				180×
450×		2÷			
		2÷	36×	4÷	

74

223

2÷	25920×			2÷
	2000×			
	36×	240×	24×	
4÷		3÷		30×

224

3÷		4800×		
48×			360×	2÷
		51840×		
150×	18×			
2÷				

75

225

× ÷

4320×	3÷		96×		120×
	2÷			10×	
60×	24×		450×		
4÷				2÷	

226

× ÷

2÷		360×			
12×	2÷	12960×		45×	
				120×	
			12×		
150×				2÷	
				2÷	

227

× ÷

12×		1296×		5÷	
20×			1440×		48×
600×		40×			
2÷					3÷

228

× ÷

2÷		4320×	150×		
18×			2÷		
		23040×			
			90×		
15×					
	2÷		3÷		

229

× ÷

360×	24×		6×		40×
		30×			
		1440×	2÷	4÷	
					3÷
			5×		
	20×			2÷	

230

× ÷

2÷		9600×		2÷	
					57600×
24×		60×			
			3÷	2÷	
5÷					
	18×				

231

2÷	3+	24×		8+	
		10×	2÷		1
5−	15×		1−	9+	
		3÷		24×	
1−			8+	2÷	3÷
5	2−				

232

5+		5	2÷	8×	3÷
5	4+				
4−		2−	5÷		3×
2−	6×		1−		
		7+		8+	
2−		2÷		10+	

233

+ − × ÷

20×		7+		2÷	3÷
9+	5+	10×			
		4	6÷		1−
2×	1−		7+	5÷	
	5−	3−			6+
5			1−		

234

+ − × ÷

9+			1−	15×	10+
6	20×				
6×		11+			
10+	30×		2−		2÷
	1−		5÷	4	
	4+			3÷	

235

$+ - \times \div$

3÷	11+			12×	10+
	5−	4÷			
10×		2÷		8+	
	3	4−	12+		2−
30×					
9+				6+	

236

$+ - \times \div$

4×	13+		1	2−	
		2÷		3×	1−
3÷		13+			
10+		5÷		2×	
1−			11+	12+	
	3×				

+ − × ÷

8+	1−		4×	12×	
		1		4−	10+
12×		1−			
10+		2÷		9+	
	12×				12+
5÷		3÷			

+ − × ÷

10+	6	8+	2−		3÷
			1−		
2÷	2−		3÷		12+
	9+			24×	
30×		4×			
11+			4−		

239

+ − × ÷

11+	3÷	5×	7+		
			15×		1−
	8+	11+			
5÷		13+	2÷		2−
			10×	15+	
3−		2			

240

+ − × ÷

1−		10+	3÷	20×	
2−				15×	1−
	5	4×			
8+			10+	2÷	13+
13+					
	5÷		2−		

241

$+ - \times \div$

120×			9+		1−
150×				18+	
	2÷	2−			
			288×		5÷
4÷	11+			300×	

242

$+ - \times \div$

480×		1−		90×	
	5÷		24×		2÷
	9+				
		600×		9+	
3−			120×		
2÷					

84

243

$+ - \times \div$

3÷		2−	14+		
2÷	13+			360×	
			60×		
60×				6÷	
		144×	5		1−
30×					

244

$+ - \times \div$

32×	10+			120×	
		3−			10+
		300×		120×	
14+			3÷		
2÷					2−
		3÷			

245

$+ - \times \div$

2	10+	1−		100×	1−
		30×			
72×					19+
150×			2÷		
	2÷	4÷			
		180×			

246

$+ - \times \div$

1−		3600×		10+	
3−					2÷
	18×		5×	600×	
3÷					
		1−			
11+			2÷		

86

247

48×	2÷		5÷		180×
	3200×				
	6×				
			3−		
20+			22+		

248

5÷		600×		36×	
10+	2÷				1−
	30×			96×	
			1−		
2÷	2160×			9+	

249

$+ - \times \div$

1−	120×			15×	
	2÷	2−			
150×			4÷	36×	11+
		15+			
2÷					
	30×			2÷	

250

$+ - \times \div$

5÷		360×	15+		8+
17+					
				4÷	
		3−	54×	3−	
3÷	1−				120×

251

+

```
8    16        17        4
                    4     13
6    14    7                   12
              14
16        6    10        15
11                            15
          3    5
```

252

+

```
4    18    12    6     13
                             16
4              10              8
     9     17              9
14             15
          12        18    8
                              3
```

253

+

8	10	9	12			5
			8		14	
16						6
	10	16		6	12	
			4		7	
11				15		7
10			10			

254

+

9		7	13	2	16	3
11	16					
			13	5		17
11	12			15	12	
	10					
	15			9		

255

+

9			10		16	
14				4		6
15	17					7
		14				
8		9			16	
8	10		19	6		
					8	

256

+

9	13		8		5	
	16		8		4	16
8		7		13		
		10			14	
9						
10	14			13	12	
		7				

257

+

10			12	10	13	
15		5				14
	8					
6		11	14		9	12
			10			
13		8			4	
11				11		

258

+

15	14	6		12		
				17	12	
	16	9				8
6				4		
		9			19	
8			13			
14			3	11		

259

+

12	12			11		13
	9		3		11	
		18				
8			13	14		
17		4			7	14
				17		
13						

260

+

6		15	11		7	6
7	9					18
			7			
14	10	8	12		11	
						3
	10	10	15			
				17		

93

261

+

```
9       26   13          15
    17
        13       4       8
14               17
4        15
             25
16
```

262

+

```
18  13          24   3   10
    6
        16       18
                 21
11  14      4
    13      25
```

94

263

+

11			19			
27		15		19		
						9
		9	4	20		
16						
		10	25	12		

264

+

15			20			
18	9	7	10			
			21			3
			29	12		
9			18			
	12				13	

265

+

13		15			5	
	6	12	13			
			12		22	
13					26	
4		20				
23	12					

266

+

17	24				15	
		7			8	
	14					24
7			15	9		
28						
		11				
		11			6	

267

+

32	7			16		22
7		8		12		
	22					
	5		20			
8		12		17		
					8	

268

+

14	10		9			19
		18				
	26		26			
				20		
12					17	
		17				3
5						

269

+

13	14		21	15	5	
						13
16					4	
	20			23		
	11					
		6	15		19	
1						

270

+

13		21		20		
	19				4	
				12		
13				10		
13	6	23		8	13	15
			6			

98

271

+

26			19		7
17					
3		21			
	15		7	9	6
12					
14	20		4		16

272

+

30				3	9
4	34				
	2		24		
					12
12	6	9	16		
13					
	11		11		

273

+

13	26		5	9	10	
		22	24			9
8			8	31		
10						7
14						

274

+

11	11			32		10
	10	14	20	7		
						10
6			18		24	
12						
11						

275

+

5		10	9		2	18
10			9			
		13		20		11
10					11	
	20					
11		4		5	14	
	14					

276

+

6	17			13		38
		8				
14					5	
	8			18		
		20				12
13						
	14				10	

277

+

11	6			16		
		16			11	6
15		20				
	3				11	13
25				7		
10	19					
				7		

278

+

15		29		13	12	
		18				7
					4	
11		9			11	
	10					13
17			9			
	6		12			

102

279

+

6		35			
38			8	7	
8	5				2
				26	
			24		
7	16				
	14				

280

+

8	18				8
		23			
29			32		7
7				8	
17				19	
	3				
8		9			

281

+

34	15			21	4	
		39	7		5	
9		14				
			24	19		
	5					

282

+

38		8	8		13	22
	14					
		24			9	3
2		8		4		
13					13	
			17			

104

283

+

14		32		5	9	
29			22			3
		22	17	27		
				4		
		7				
				5		

284

+

8	10	13			7	
				11	12	
4		22			9	14
19			43			
	3					
10		11				

285

+

29	10				35	
	7	25				
		6		42		
18						
		9				
7			4		4	

286

+

10			43		10	
13						
15			33		7	
	15				26	4
3						
	11			6		

287

+

20	18				43
8			23	9	
36				10	
	7				
		22			

288

|

10		7		17	
18					10
6	13	14	14		
			15	9	
46					11

289

+

32				4	
8		16	5	53	
	26				10
		10			
	12		6		
		14			

290

+

6		53	15		15
6				31	
	4				
	20		13		
16		13			
				4	

291

×

21			60	12		5
98				18		56
	120					
60		30	21		24	
	48					
12			42	20	35	6

292

×

30		24		42		168
21		10		120		
6	105			8		
80		252		6	42	15
12						
		140				

293

×

84			12			60
15	18	12		70		
					28	
	40		35	36		
12		3			140	72
	7					
140			12			

294

×

40	90	14			4	72
			42			
	2	35			42	
126		60				
	20		12	60		70
		168			36	
1						

110

295

×

210		30	84		8	
	6					126
40		12			210	
		16				
	140		42		54	40
18						
		7	10			

296

×

84		84	15		60	28
30						
	40		8		63	
						6
56	18		210	42		
	15			24	40	

297

×

84			18		40	
24		20		84		42
36			70			
				5	3	
70	84			72		4
	15		4			
			210			

298

×

70		21	18		8	
	24			60		
60		30	112		2	21
	36		105		120	
		8		12	7	
7					15	

112

299

×

70			120		9	
140		84				24
12			21		20	
	6					
36			42		56	5
10	12					
		20		126		

300

×

4	84		35			36
14	60		90		72	
		7				
		24		8		140
90	42					
		120	12		35	

301

×

180			392		75
	392	36	12		
	32	15		240	252
90	210			168	

302

×

72		315	112		240
	20				
		84		90	
14					
	12	20		252	
105		48			210

114

×

140	400		18			84
				252		
	6					
24		504	56		30	
			150			
3		294			240	

×

56		20		378		
		70			420	24
360				4		
	252					
	30			150		
42		72			2	
				28		

305

×

252			42	90		360
	70			80		
	120		16		245	
72						56
	105			216		

306

×

42		240	140			90
8					84	
		35		9		
120						
210		72	144		210	
						56

307

×

150	84		126	144	140	
		96				
			42	10		90
196						
	30		120	3		336

308

×

5		216			56	
14	30			140		180
112		12				60
180		28		90		
			504			
					7	

309

×

5	504			12	140	
						12
72		420			315	
			4			
280	180				168	
			210	24		

310

×

36	84		210		12
	210		300		
	96				
			8		35
35	252		72		
				84	
	120				

118

311

×

36			16800		
90	12	42			1176
		144			
	31360				
			30		3
				420	
	15				

312

×

21		42		30	32	
5040						504
		1080				
					29400	70
	24					
		80			9	

313

×

30		84	24		56	
28			60		15	
	144					84
		17640		20		
15						
					90	
8			21			

314

×

8		2520	21		120	
120						3
		4		42		
70			360		28	2520
36			140			
3						

315

×

30	24		280		
	840		21		36
			6720		
				90	24
		42				30
30		42			28	

316

×

4		6720		68040		30
	28					
105					84	
	3150		192	56		
18						
				10		

121

317

×

576		4410			
	25200			21	
			20		
1050		72		36	
					80
	84		84		
				2	

318

×

84	24		140		6	
				105		
7200	576					35
	35	210			36	
3				42		96

319

×

6	88200				12	
6	30		168			7056
	20	576		900		
196					30	

320

×

70		168	40			252
				6	3	
504	120					
		6720			120	
						35
30	9		84			

123

321

×

3024	30			42		
		30		60	56	
						42
30		12	20160			
56		35				30
	12					

322

×

30			36	168		10
25200						
6		9408			5	
						84
6			10			
196	360					18

323

×

84		20			14112	56
	30		30			
30					3780	
	3					
	24		4			
28	7560				10	

324

×

40		2646			24	
30				20		12
	21					
		20	1260			
7056			240	56		
				3		30

325

×

20			36288			
35			6			
37800		72		40		
			105			
24				84	7	
168		20				

326

×

79380				40		
	4800		4			
			294		36	
12						
	630	20				
112		6		30	42	

327

×

8064			30			6
		60	210		28	
				9072		
60		3				700
	42					
70						
				48		

328

×

21			4200			12
24		5040				
42				120		
20						
	105			6	36	84
	20		168			

329

×

20		21		2520		
14	24		12			
		840			12	
		30				20
72	17640					
						3
	42			20		

330

×

900				112		
	28	36		10		
				2520		8820
60		42				
168					12	
		720				

331

+ −

5+		3−	9+	10+	20+
	15+				
17+			6+	10+	
		7	13+		15+
1−	2−				
	5−		19+	2−	
9+				2−	

332

+ −

17+		15+		4+	
1−		8+	1−	11+	
	9+				
10+	1−	11+		2−	
		5−		15+	4−
	5+	17+	2		
			14+		

129

333

+ −

14+		5−		2−	9+	
	15+	4+				15+
2−		16+		1		
	6−			3−	13+	
2−		3+				11+
	11+			1−		
14+		7+				

334

+ −

6+			14+	1−	19+	
1−	7					2−
	4−		5−		14+	
16+		8+				
	12+	11+	13+			9+
			18+		6+	
2−						

130

335

+ −

13+			19+		8+	
15+	4−	9+		12+		
					10+	4
	2−	11+				
7+		5−		1−		3−
	12+			17+	15+	
	1−					

336

+ −

1−	14+			13+		2−
	13+	10+				
7		5−	8+		5−	
16+			2−		7+	6
		7+		15+		
11+			13+		1−	
					4−	

+ −

12+		3−	5−		10+
1−			12+	7+	
	6+		3−		12+
6−			3		
17+		14+	2−	2−	13+
5+			4+		
		13+			

+ −

3−	1−	4+		15+	
		4−		9+	
12+			1−		11+
5+		14+		10+	6−
	1−				
14+		6+	15+		2−
			3		2−

339

+ −

4−		5	4−		10+
15+	7+	14+		1−	
			14+	1−	
	4−			13+	
11+			11+	4−	11+
8+		19+			5−
				1−	

340

+ −

12+			4−		2−
5−	13+	17+	1−		12+
			10+		
2−			11+		8+
	9+		12+		10+
2−	12+			19+	5
					2−

341

+ −

2−	22+			7+		6−
		6+			13+	
6+	5−		12+			
		21+		5−		15+
14+			1−	20+		
	5+					
		9+		1−		

342

+ −

1−	3+	2−		5−	12+	
		25+				28+
11+				12+		
		4−				
1−		4+		4−		
9+		19+			16+	4+

343

+ −

16+			12+	8+	
13+	20+			19+	
	15+				5−
11+			1−		
1−		4−		7	
12+			25+		1−
	4−				

344

+ −

2	22+		14+		
20+				20+	15+
		13+			
14+					2−
			18+		
	9+	3−	5−	5−	
			1−		13+

135

345

+ −

12+			10+	20+	2−	
	21+					4−
25+		7+	5−			
				4−	17+	
		1−				
6+	7+	6−	25+			

346

+ −

2−	17+	13+	4−	
		18+	1−	25+
22+				
		13+	10+	
			11+	6−
20+	17+			
5−				

347

2−		6−		22+	3−	
12+		2−				6+
28+			1	2−		
		9+		13+		
		4−		15+		
	7+		8+			6+
1−		5−				

348

3−		13+	12+		1−	
3−				26+		
	20+				3+	
16+			2−		16+	16+
	1−					
	11+	12+			19+	

137

349

+ −

2−		7	22+		2−	
15+			2−		5−	
6−				13+	27+	
17+		3−				
	6−					
13+		14+	13+		11+	

350

+ −

6+			17+	16+		
2−				2−	4−	2−
5−	6−		25+			
				25+		
13+		2−		11+		
		13+			2−	
21+						

351

+ −

1−		4+		14+	20+	
10+	18+					14+
		9+				
	6+		4−		1−	
43+			6−			7+
				3−		
					2−	

352

+ −

14+	4+		31+			6−
		1	18	3		
11+						14+
18+				7+		
4−		15+	2−			
4+				12+		

353

+ −

12+	5+	2−		18+		
		31+				
				5−	6−	
1−	16+		33+		20+	10+
				8+	9+	
4−						

354

+ −

18+	6−	12+		3−		3−
		14+			13+	
			6−			
1−				14+		23+
8+			22+			
4−				14+		
	5−					

140

355

+ −

1−	16+	41+			1−
					23+
13+		5+			30+
17+		1−	5−		
1−			7+		
	1				

356

+ −

18+	14+		14+	6−	12+
				6 ı	
		18+		16+	
2−			10+		
	30+			1−	3−
			14+		
		1−		3+	

357

+ −

10+	13+			15+	1−
	6+				17+
		1−	12+		43+
3−			16+	1−	
20+					
11+		2−		5−	

358

+ −

16+		28+	4+		
34+					
				2	
15+	15+	3+	1−	3−	
			1−	15+	
	1−	4−			
		6+			

359

2−	17+	11+		15+		4−
		6−	10+	49+		
13+				4+		
10+	12+					
	9+	1−	2−			
				11+		

360

12+	11+	21+	6−	1−		24+
				12+		
			1−			
2−	27+	10+		17+		
					20+	
		1−				
	10+				3−	

361

3−		34+	4+	8+	6−
21+					4−
				5	18+
			19+		
		15+			
3−	14+			2−	1−
			1−		

362

11+		5+		15+	10+
15+				6−	1−
	28+		8+		
		2−			
12+	2		3−	21+	1−
	5+				
	7+			2−	

144

363

+ −

2−	19+		9+		10+	
	23+		13+		9+	
15+	4		1−		20+	
		4−		41+		
1−					11+	2−

364

+ −

15+		4+		2−		
33+						
1−	3−	11+			6−	
			3−			
10+		1−		15+		
	12+	5+			14+	
		4−		7+		

145

365

34+	6				43+
				1−	
3−		6−			
1−		12+	7+		
12+	23+				9+
	11+		13+		
				1−	

366

11+			17+	10+	
14+	3−			1−	9+
		17+	14+		
2−		6			
13+			1−	36+	8+
3−	8+	3−			

367

+ −

11+	1−	18+	36+		1−	
					10+	
	2−				14+	
13+		27+				
						11+
4−					12+	
7	10+		1−			

368

+ −

31+			10+		10+	
	3−			1−	10+	
		19+				2−
2−	16+			7+		
		2−			42+	
7+	12+					
			8+			

369   + −

21+				11+		14+
	42+		6		1−	
			4−			
6−		1−	7+	4−	31+	
						7+
		15+				
			10+			

370   + −

1−		21+	8+		20+	12+
2−						
			1−	30+		
4−		1−		6+		6−
16+			17+			
	6−				2−	
1−		6				

371

×÷

6×	210×			30×	4÷	
		112×				84×
36×			30×			
	7	45×		4÷		5÷
140×			84×			
	2÷	2÷		120×		126×
		3÷				

372

×÷

4×		150×		42×		
	36×			245×	36×	6÷
2÷						
210×			2÷	2÷		140×
90×		2÷				
84×			6÷		20×	3
		84×				

149

373

×÷

84×			20×		42×	2÷
5÷		4				
42×			120×		30×	
18×		2÷		168×		
	210×		21×		4÷	
		30×			2÷	
2÷				105×		

374

×÷

2÷		210×		42×		80×
18×						
56×	90×	2÷		105×	2÷	
		16×				7÷
		42×		60×		
120×				4÷		6
	105×				2÷	

375

× ÷

2÷		60×	3÷	196×		2÷
35×					40×	
	140×		48×	3÷		
					108×	
28×			140×	30×		
36×					7÷	
3	2÷			120×		

376

× ÷

90×		30×	48×	4÷		35×
	56×					
			6÷		42×	
1	140×			2÷		
48×	2÷		175×		6×	
		7÷				120×
7÷		24×				

151

377

× ÷

80×	12×		3÷		70×	
			6	84×		3÷
70×				36×		
3÷	140×					120×
	2÷	42×	2÷			
42×			100×		7÷	
				48×		

378

× ÷

2÷	60×		35×	126×		4÷
				42×		
5÷	72×					70×
	1	84×	48×			
126×				5÷		
	42×	5÷	60×		16×	2÷

379

×÷

210×		2÷		2÷		28×
	24×	30×	60×		7÷	
			3÷			
63×				2÷		30×
	20×		42×			
4÷		84×	6	70×	60×	

380

×÷

126×	60×		6×		140×	
		4÷				72×
	105×			2÷		
2÷		84×	30×			
20×			140×		36×	
	7÷	24×				5÷
			2÷		7	

153

381

× ÷

180×			360×	2÷	7÷	
	168×				420×	
28×						180×
	5÷		14×	720×		
				504×		
420×	3÷					
					2÷	

382

× ÷

2÷		5÷		36×	420×	
252×						
	420×			336×		
	3÷			280×		
180×					3÷	6×
105×		168×	2÷			
				10×		

154

383

$\times \div$

1050×			2÷		3÷	
	120×		2÷	1008×		
3÷				245×		120×
168×						
168×		60×	2÷	35×		
				144×		

384

$\times \div$

2÷	3÷	3÷		980×		10×
			336×			
70×			80×	3÷		
					2÷	
180×		180×			56×	
7×				60×		
	168×					

155

385

× ÷

4÷		20×	504×		105×
504×			12×		
100×				3÷	
		294×			2÷
72×	2÷		140×		
		150×			96×
7÷					

386

× ÷

288×		210×		105×	
	2÷		6÷		
	504×	7÷		360×	120×
245×					
		24×	2÷		
	120×		420×		
3÷					

387

120×	2÷		56×		5÷
			315×	288×	
24×		490×			
				2÷	
210×		4÷		126×	420×
	180×				
		2÷			

388

252×	40×			54×	840×
84×			630×		120×
2÷		5÷		420×	
	28×				
		540×			2÷
			2÷		7÷

389

168×			12×	6÷	980×	
1260×	3÷					2÷
		60×				
			2÷		630×	
2÷		210×				144×
2÷	525×			12×		

390

45×		84×		120×		2÷
					210×	
3÷	420×					
	2÷			210×		378×
56×		90×				
			420×	2÷		
					2÷	

158

391

3528×	21168×				30×	
	10×		33600×			
			2	180×		
70×		12×				
		60×			7÷	6÷
2÷			2÷			

392

5÷		210×	2352×			
72×					2÷	360×
	12×		90×			
840×		84×				
				48×		140×
		2÷				
	35×				2÷	

393

× ÷

252×	24×		2÷		37800×
20×				35280×	252×
	2÷				
2÷	21×			20×	
		1050×			36×
			4÷		

394

× ÷

30240×	5×		6	105×	3÷
		56×		42×	
					450×
	1008×	1680×			
2÷					
			3÷	240×	
				28×	

160

395

× ÷

168×		2÷		20×			
		840×					
	15×			7056×			
30×		2÷					
2÷	3÷		5×		252×		
		28×		60×			
210×					6×		

396

× ÷

15×		2÷	240×	210×	2÷	
	140×					84×
32256×				42×		
		30×				
21×					3÷	
					120×	
28×		30×				

397

× ÷

15×		23040×		2268×		168×
14×						
			40×	5÷		
						504×
180×		7÷				
	35×		4÷			60×
		42×				

398

× ÷

42×	2÷		560×			30×
		756×	5040×			
600×						
		84×			5÷	
					144×	
42×		1440×				
					7÷	

162

399

× ÷

2÷		2400×			70×	
		1008×	48×			
42×						52920×
	105×			3÷		
		480×				
				20×		2÷
	42×					

400

× ÷

12600×		7÷	3÷		140×	
2			2592×			
			60×			
14×		5184×				84×
20×				980×		
	3÷					
					5×	

401

× ÷

6÷		3150×	40×		42×
1260×					
	2	30×		168×	72×
	140×				
		4÷	3528×		
3÷					60×
	2÷				

402

× ÷

6÷	42×		3÷		80×
		5	70560×		
80640×	42×		10×		
				2÷	
5÷			36×	588×	
3÷				5×	

403

× ÷

28×	30240×	30×	35×			8400×
			2÷		3÷	
			84×			
		6×				
42×		4÷	60×			
			1260×		72×	

404

× ÷

840×					2÷	20×
4		3528×				
30×						
60×		3360×		420×		
21×						2÷
			42×	3÷		
				40×		

165

405

× ÷

2÷	1260×					
	105×		2520×			
3÷			20×			
12×				9072×		350×
140×	12×					
		12×				
21×			2÷			

406

× ÷

42×		30×		3600×		
24×			2÷		7÷	
	23520×					
3÷		30×		84×		
				6×		4÷
40×		3024×			105×	

407

× ÷

6300×			96×	12×		1680×
84×						
		525×				
3÷	3÷				2520×	
		10080×	6×			
				14×		
2÷						

408

× ÷

84×		41160×	1800×			
					20×	
12×		2÷				
720×			350×			
				48×	18×	
				196×		
	4÷		2÷			

409

$\times \div$

2÷	140×	1260×	60×	84×		5÷
144×			42×			
					13440×	
1960×						
				180×		12×
			3÷			

410

$\times \div$

288×		20×		30×	7÷	
					63×	
2520×			960×			
			52920×		2÷	
2÷						5040×
		3÷		140×		

168

411

+ − × ÷

2−	4÷	16+		60×
11+	56×	3×		
			1−	
13+	16+		42×	12×
	16×	1−	13+	
		20×		
2÷		4	7÷	

412

+ − × ÷

7÷	30×	13+	2÷	
18+			1−	
4−	9×	2−	245×	
	13+	10×	1	
	42×		2÷	
12+	20×		30×	
		17+		

413

+ − × ÷

2−	2÷	3	35×	70×	12+
		12×			
4−			120×		
12+	196×	13+		12×	
			1−	3÷	
11+				294×	
15×		2÷			

414

+ − × ÷

13+	2÷		84×	150×	
	60×		36×	7÷	
	6				11+
13+		96×	3−	4−	
	11+				
2÷	60×	5×	1−		
			13+		

170

415

+ − × ÷

140×		3−		6÷	12×	
2÷		11+	14+			294×
	2÷					
10+			84×	30×		8+
	2−					
	42×		30×	2−		
5				13+		

416

+ − × ÷

30×		21×			28×	1−
	12+					
9+			1−		14+	
14+	84×		3÷		30×	
			15×			2÷
2÷	175×			2−	126×	
			1			

417

+ − × ÷

9+ 4	1	1- 7	6	30× 2	5	1- 3
14+ 1	4	11+ 6	5	56× 7	3	2
6	7	2÷ 1	63× 3	4	2	30× 5
15× 5	36× 6	2	7	3	3- 4	1
3	2	11+ 4	5÷ 1	5	7	6
14× 7	3	5	2	36× 6	4÷ 1	4
2	60× 5	3	4	1	6	7 7

418

+ − × ÷

13+		5× 1	2÷	140×		2 2
	1	5			70× 2	7
42×		112×		4-	10+	5
	14+		5÷ 15			
8+			15	12+		1- 34
	84×			2-		31
	56×				6÷	

419

+ − × ÷

11+		5÷		42×	
	1−	7	9+		1−
60×		13+	24×	7÷	
				72×	21×
14+	245×				
	6×		60×		
			5÷		2−

420

+ − × ÷

42×		16+	15+		4÷
	24×			70×	
			1−		3	60×
4÷	30×	6−		72×	2−
175×	11+			28×		10+
		2÷			

173

421

+ − × ÷

7÷		252×	2÷	180×	
13+			14+		
	2−	294×			2−
			5÷	294×	
150×	48×	12+			
					84×
	5−				

422

+ − × ÷

1−		168×	2÷		1−
252×		12+			
		7÷		1−	
5−	11+	96×			21+
	180×		588×		
240×					
		5÷			

174

423

+ − × ÷

2−		84×		9+	
6÷		980×			
2÷	252×	5÷	54×		2−
		40×			
11+		252×		3−	60×
	19+				

424

+ − × ÷

180×		80×	84×		7÷	
			9+		16+	
						168×
2−	3÷	168×				
				2−		180×
18+		50×	2−			
4÷						

425

30×	168×		13+		588×
1−	2÷		3+	420×	
	4÷				4−
98×		180×	15+		
			700×	6÷	1−

426

3−		4÷	12+		294×
6+					18+
3−	168×		180×	2÷	
10+		252×		140×	1−
					120×
	12+		6÷		

+ − × ÷

6−	72×			70×		120×
	2−	5−				
150×		19+			120×	
				2÷		
504×		2−			17+	
	150×		7÷			
				2÷		

+ − × ÷

4÷	1−		210×	16+		17+
				75×		
294×		210×	2÷			
				4÷		
		180×			24×	17+
1−	2−					
	12+					

429

+ − × ÷

672×		1−		525×		
	210×	168×		2÷		
			8+		120×	
		150×			21+	
1−						
2−	3−	1176×			2÷	
					2÷	

430

+ − × ÷

1−	3−		5÷		3÷	
	210×	1−		252×	10+	
22+					18+	
18×		11+				
	180×			245×		13+
2÷						

431

2÷		105×	1890×			28×
22+	1−					
		180×	2÷			
				60480×		
		2÷	13+	1−		
2−						
	12+					

432

2÷		15+			4−	
15÷	3÷	1−		7+	34+	2−
		70×	2×			
	45×		28×			
86400×		7÷				

179

433

+ − × ÷

20+				1−		21×
30+	2÷	3÷		3÷		
		28×	2520×			2−
	2−					
		5−		50×	15+	
					21+	

434

+ − × ÷

10+	3−		30+			7÷
		1−		2÷		
15×			10+			96×
	8×			1−		
		20160×			20×	
294×				3÷		9+

435

70×	80×		3÷		84×	
		4−	36×			
	3÷		3−		2−	
2÷		29+		896×		
	11+			19+		
12+						
					8+	

436

1−		5×	24+			54000×
2−						
	27+				17+	
		2÷				
				2÷	10×	
90×	2−		32×			6×
				7÷		

437

+ − × ÷

30×		13+		6720×	6+	3360×
	42×					
6÷		5÷				
	504×					
			3−	108×		
24+	2÷				1−	1−

438

+ − × ÷

11+		6÷		2−	14+
14+		2÷		50×	
	4×	5400×			
			336×		
4−		2016×			
700×	4−			3÷	

182

439

$+ - \times \div$

3528×	432×			2−		10080×
				12+		
				2÷		
8+	2÷	2−	1−			
				21×		
	75×	17+		252×		2÷

440

$+ - \times \div$

2520×					3−	90720×
360×						
			4÷			
	196×	7+				
13+			63×	5÷		6×
	2−				14+	
	3−		4÷			

441

+ − × ÷

105×	10+			17+	6÷
		3−			2−
2÷			24+	540×	1−
28224×					
				175×	
30×					
	13+			2÷	

442

+ − × ÷

7÷		2−		1−	30+
36×	175×		2÷		
				30+	14+
43200×	42×				
3−			84×		2÷

443

+ − × ÷

4−	1152×				1225×
	72000×	28+			
					2÷
		2÷			
		6−	42×		13+
	84×		15+		

444

+ − × ÷

36288×	7875×	2÷		6−	2÷
			24×		
	5−			15×	3−
8+			294×	35+	
	12+	2÷			

445

+ − × ÷

					2−	
29+						
	28800×		70×		2÷	
72×		20×		27+	2−	
		3−				
		3÷	4÷		3−	9+
			9+			

446

+ − × ÷

12+			12600×		22+	
2÷		13440×			84×	
	25×		4÷			
			3−		40×	
			3−	6÷		11+
1−						

186

447

+ − × ÷

10+		28×	6÷	11+
98×		2700×		52920×
12×	2520×	5÷		4−
			12+	
		2−		
3−		7÷		

448

+ − × ÷

11+	4÷	21+		28×
			2÷	
	60×	63504×	245×	1−
2−				
		24+		6÷
10×				
3−			20×	

449

$+ - \times \div$

2÷		9+	2−	29+	14+
15120×					
	4÷				10+
	75×				
45360×			3÷	9+	
					1−
3−					

450

$+ - \times \div$

2−	75600×		13+	8+	
	11+	6+			
			35×	140×	
2−	2÷	6−			
		3÷			
3÷	140×	20×	432×		

451

+

17		6		11		11	10
19		14		17			
		8		4			
1			7		21		
12	15			17	11		
	10				14		11
		18	8		17		
3				6			

452

I

10	7	11		8		22	
			9		8	6	
		17	23		5		7
18						14	
	13	13	10				
12			8		10		
	12				13		8
		5	9		10		

453

+

9			12		23	8	
10		7					15
8				20			
16	10	21	14		8		
				12			11
		11		15		7	
17		14					
6				4		10	

454

+

6	12	15		15	15		
			15			2	11
23		5			19		
			5	3			
9		15		11	12	9	
9	13						14
		14	15			16	
				5			

455

+

7	6		6	8		14	15
10		10			12		
	19		11				4
		14		10		12	
12			17				
9	14			12	12		17
	7						
		8	10		12		

456

+

6		13	12	10		21	13
	4			15			
10							11
10	18		20		5		
				8	6	5	
11	12	15					10
			15			15	
15		8					

191

457

+

20		4	14			19	5
9				15			
	4				20		12
9		19	17		15		
10				5		8	
	9	8					
12			20		1	9	14
	10						

458

+

10		10		9	15	6	
10	12						11
	7	17		16		17	
6					10		10
	7		7	4			
12	14			9		11	
	10	16	8			17	
				7			

192

459

+

5	15			8		11	
	13		19	17			4
11	13				15		
		10				19	
23			25				
	10					20	
		19					
10					21		

460

I

12	29			6		10	12
			28	3			
19	5	12					
			3	11		10	
					17	13	13
12		6	8				
9				19	11		8
	12						

461

+

9	11		30		4		6
	16				31		
				16		7	
5	9					9	5
16	27	9		13			
					9		23
	8	4					
				8		13	

462

+

20	15	6	6			27	
				10			
			8		25		
14		17				8	
22				6	11	4	
	13		23			13	
					13		6
14		7					

194

463

18	8	8	11		11		7
				9	20	15	
	8	12					14
	7			29			
		15				5	5
22							
27					13		14
		10					

464

20		22					15
		11			7		
6	20		10		23		7
		22			7		
10		3		15			18
11	24				12		4
	3		18				

465

+

9	9		19			20
		27			7	
15				9		
	6	7	14		9	14
21			22			
	15		6			20
	18			7		14

466

+

8	20			9		4	17
	13	8		10			
		18	5		7		
16	13			12	22	9	
		11					
				11			15
11	9			31			
		9					

467

+

19	28				31		
				15			
3	17					4	
11		21			36		
			20				
4						10	
9		18			9		
10				23			

468

+

28				10	28		9
15	8						
	30	10				14	
			15		13		
5	24	28			3	8	
		1		14		10	15

197

469

+

32			23		23	17	
10							
13				3			
	29	13			6		
				32			
10		18					
18		11		9		15	
6							

470

+

24	7		10	21	15		
4		12				5	
	24		23				
28						11	
			36				
	5						
14	12				15		
	17		5				

198

+

17	26			11		6
	9		8	23		
		5				9
14		29		8	25	
15				20	11	
		11	6			3
8			12		12	

+

14	20	14			12	
			20			
	19	32	9	11		
			7	23		
7			36		8	
		15				
	8					
10		12		11		

473

+

35		3		13		21	
		9		6		32	
6		19					13
				14			
9		5		32			
		7	24				
14							
	11			7		8	

474

+

6	10		6	16		14	4
		11		12			
4	33				32		8
					10		
19		20					
12						6	
	22			31			12

200

475

+

12	4	33	13		12		14
	15			8		25	
							12
18		9					
	10	31					
11			32	10		8	
6							
5							

476

+

11	23		22			19
	20		17			
				13	19	
19	38				14	
11			15			
6			17			
15				9		

201

477

+

11	31		21		7	11	
		8				22	
10			16				15
					41		
		19	9				10
8							
	22		7				8
			12				

478

+

6		13	14			32	7
12			6				
7				40			
					11	20	
28		26					
3		15					
				15	4		
12			3		14		

479

+

480

+

481

×

168	60		48			84	
			120		2		1
8	84			84		320	
	240		6		105		
						28	
48		40		96			
15			21		40		72
	56						

482

×

72		2	48		28	40	
	56	90		42		6	
160							56
	60		20				
		56		30		144	
7			96			84	
		56		90			
6					160		

483

×

112		120	24			15	
			7		40	60	
72			144			7	
60		56		56			64
						18	
12	210		42	240			
	8					56	
			5	96			

484

×

240	24		7		120		48
				105			
48			120		56	6	
30	448						35
				144	4		
84	3	24				210	
				16			192
	140						

485

× (multiplication)

3	30		168			160	
		48		12	112		
245						12	
	6			112	120		40
144		105					
128				24		6	
		60					84
4	7		120				

486

× (multiplication)

96		3		70		336	
14		30				48	
		5	16		12		
120	40	84	392				60
				18			
			120		48		
36				48	56		
112					5		

206

487

×

42 48 210 40
15 84 192
64 6
96 7 35
15 60 192
56 96 18
96 50 98
24

488

×

80 56 200 36 12
42
12 28 120 3 112
144
96 24 42 70
48 30
35 105 128
48

489

×

120			288	168			
7						40	
252	560			18	480		
		210					112
96				560			
					48		70
192		240					
					18		

490

×

420			120			576	96
2352		15					
			28				
		240		320			
96			105		240		168
			216				
	32			336			35

491

×

140	12		84			120	192
			420				
576		180			336		
						8	
126			1536			525	
				120			
	35			512		84	

492

×

384	21		30	2	120		
		8				840	
168				56	48		
		180			200	14	
	420						
		192				48	
	40	336	72		21		

493

×

8	448		216			60	
		60		168		210	
	80						
			576		168		
35		252					672
	4		140		16		
432			40				
				10			

494

×

112		672	360	720			96
120					42		
	175			560		288	
240	192		2				
				294		70	
	18			768			

495

×

1280	40			126			
		108		40		168	
	168				288		40
72		392					
				840		120	
		80					672
210					24		

496

×

72			240		48		140
35				2			
	56	10	144		672	36	
144		24	280		40		
				588			
48			280			240	6

497

×

16	160		42		24		30
	36			112	30		
						70	
4		2352		336			144
40							
1512			7200				
			53760				

498

×

24	4032			10			160
				84			
	40	56	30			126	
				36			6720
105	480		192				
					4		
			24	240			84
14							

499

×

96			9000	168			12
168				7			
	84			4	6720		
80							
		12		2304	48		
14			112		450		
5040							
						4	

500

×

30		168			20		48
	47040	64				210	
		54	10				
			10		16		72
	92160	7		32			
						42	
				84			
		168			30		

501

×

48		18		30		448	
28		280		2880			
	15		1680			6	
168			12		64	6	
	210						40
320				56		63	
	24						

502

×

192	19600		30	14	24		6
					90		
			128				
		18			84		2800
	192		280				
42	72						168
		240		96			

214

×

12	4		3360				180
				24	42		
16800			2352				16
192		30		40			1120
			288	3			
42		112					12
				30			

×

1200					336		
7056						320	3
210			120	2304			
	28						
		12			12		40
24	30		112		2520		
						28	
	48						

505

×

96	56			24	90		
	2016		280		7	20	
						24	
		120					
35	3		4032		4608		210
		11520					
						56	
		10					

506

×

48	30	6720		8		96	
			20		84		
	56			42			
					42	120	
24			18			9600	
60							56
21		112					
			48		30		

507

×

2	48			42		50400	
	48	280					
		54		640		40	
60					42		
	28		60				24
	192				56		
		1008				48	
35							

508

×

120		42	168			16	
			12	20			48
24	224				75		
		25200			56		
						72	
12		80					35
42			24	192	168		

509

×

224	210		8		30	
		24		2		252
120		80640				
3360				24		
30						
			210		15680	
	72	96				
		96				

510

×

30	320		8	1080	42	
					168	
	42	140	336			48
48						
			40320	140		16
	12				90	
112						5
		48				

511

5−	16+	1−	7+		2−		12+
		3−	18+	6			
1		3−			7+		
3−		2−	1−	13+		5	
7+				12+		9+	
15+	3−		11+	18+			
			5+	6−	8+		
1−	13+				1−		

512

12+	15+		4−		2	1−	
			4−		13+	11+	
2−	8+		13+				13+
	15+				7−		
7+		13+			13+	3−	
20+		6−	7+				10+
	14+			2−		3	
		2−		18+			

513

+ −

3−		2−		1−		10+	13+
3	3+	2−	10+				
13+			3−		2		14+
		4−	1−	20+			
4−	8+		6−	1			5+
		10+		3−		10+	
1−				7−			9+
1−		6+		13+			

514

+ −

12+	4−		1−	5+	5+	9+	
	7	7−				6−	
4+			14+	1−	10+	2−	
14+	1−						10+
		11+		19+			
7+		10+		14+		2−	
	1−				1	19+	
10+		4+		14+			

+ −

20+		5	10+			2−	
	10+	6−		14+	10+		2−
		12+	1−			8	
4+	2−			11+	15+	6−	
		3−	6−				2−
7−					8+		
2−	11+		12+			7−	
		1	15+		14+		

+ −

4	10+		19+	3−	2−		5−
5−		11+			4−		
4−				1−		9+	
	13+	4+		17+			
2−			1	4−		8+	19+
	7−		5−	2−			
7	2−			1−	8+		
5−		1−				7−	

+ −

2−		3	6+		13+	6−	4+
3−	11+		17+				
				2−	16+	7−	
2−	6+	17+					5−
	1			6−		14+	
4+	17+		5+				
	18+		13+	2	5−	2−	2−
5+							

+ −

15+	10+			10+	12+		2−
	16+		4				
		1−		15+	14+		
14+		12+			2−		
	5+	8	2−		5−		9+
12+		7+			4−	12+	
	12+		2−				
	6+		4−		6	7−	

519

+ −

15+			4+		18+		
9+	26+		23+		13+	4+	
	24+	4−	17+	7−		5−	
		4+		1−	5+		
		30+				30+	
4−	3−			6+			
	2−						

520

+ −

4	6−		12+	5+	18+		
29+						16+	
1−			20+			23+	
25+		4+					
7−			23+		12+		
		10+		1−			
20+						5−	
4+		2−		3−			

521

+ −

3−		23+		20+		1−	11+
30+							
		24+	1−			1−	
6+				4	2−		7+
			4+			35+	
4+		20+					19+
	13+				7−		
		11+					

522

+ −

11+			4−	4+		13+	
18+	2−	1−		15+			1−
			11+	20+	9+		
	17+						19+
			7−		5−		
1−	6−	24+		5−		22+	6
		14+			9+		

+ −

22+	3−		10+	16+			1−
		6−		14+			
	5−		23+		6	23+	
11+		1−					14+
		29+	1−				
5−				3−		25+	14+
	3−						
11+		1−			1−		

+ −

15+		7−		8+	13+	12+
	7−	1−				4−
			32+		6−	10+
	2−					21+	6+
1−		6−		5+		
	7+		3−			6+
4−	29+			23+		
				2		

525

+ −

14+		6+	1−		18+	24+	7+
1−	7−						
	17+		8+				
20+	12+				12+	1−	
		1−	18+			31+	7
							2−
9+					1−		
	22+					11+	

526

+ −

3+		7−	16+	14+	2−		6+
27+					2−	1−	
				30+			18+
1−						7+	
22+		12+	2−				
8+			2−	1−	14+	16+	
		3					7−
9+		16+			10+		

226

527

+ −

16+		3−		9+		11+	
	28+			6+		2−	4+
9+	4+	8			4−		
		5−	4−	36+			2−
15+							
		11+	7+	31+	15+		
25+							1−

528

+ −

2−	22+		20+		1−	14+	
						6−	3−
2−		4+		8+	34+		
20+						13+	8+
		34+					
15+			16+				
					2−	7+	15+
4−			6−				

529

+ −

15+	25+			2−	16+	
	3−	32+				
				18+		
	17+		16+	7−		
	4−	6−			30+	
19+	7−	16+		7+		
	6+					
3+	15+					

530

+ −

15+		6−	14+		
17+	15+		18+		
13+	8+	6−			
	5−	44+	12+	3+	
17+			1−	1−	
28+					
	7−	15+	4+		
	3				

531

+ −

12+		20+				10+	
	4−		22+			36+	8+
2−		8+	18+				
9+	11+					4−	
		6−					2−
10+		8+				11+	
23+		8+		16+			
	2−					2−	

532

+ −

14+	16+	17+			1−	12+	
				18+		2−	7+
	46+						
4−			2−	10+		10+	
		13+		1−		23+	
			3−		1−		
2−			14+	10+	12+		7+
7+							

533

+ −

2−	4−		20+	10+		5−	
	24+					12+	14+
				6−			
5−		23+		16+			
23+					4−		1−
		13+		26+		4+	
			14+				13+
2					15+		

534

+ −

7+		3−	3−	29+	11+		
3−					28+		
16+		2−	5+			15+	
	19+				1−		
25+	9+		13+		3+	1−	12+
		20+					
			2−		13+		

230

535

+ −

2−	22+		19+				9+
	14+			3−			
		5−	32+		11+		
21+							9+
		4+	22+	19+		19+	
4+							
1−		3−					25+
	4−						

536

+ −

25+		10+	43+			4−	
			16+	6−		3−	
38+	2					4−	
				6−			
6+			1−			1−	2−
4−				14+			
		7+	4+		13+	17+	
6−			10+				

231

537

+ −

16+	1−	20+			15+		
			17+	23+		10+	
					6−	11+	
10+	23+		2−	3−			
		4−		4−	1−	4−	
14+			49+			1−	
					10+		
					4+		4

538

+ −

16+		8+			5	29+	
	7−	14+					18+
			18+		14+		
5−				7−		1−	26+
24+					16+		
3+			25+				
23+	6−						
			1−				

232

539

42+					8+	19+	
	15+	2−				15+	
			6−	3−			
7−		14+			6+		5+
21+			23+		5−		
				2−	5−	23+	
	18+						9+
1−				7−		6	

540

62+							
6+				17+			
	2−	7−			7+		3−
21+			7−	8+		10+	
		12+			24+		15+
			1−			4+	
5−		15+		2−			
12+						10+	

233

541

×÷

210×		3÷	80×		12×	168×	
	2÷					112×	
2÷		192×		75×			3÷
	210×			3÷			
168×			2÷	2÷		28×	80×
	18×						
20×	2÷		42×			90×	
		2	168×				

542

×÷

36×		10×		28×		30×	2÷
	15×	336×					
		168×		2÷	2÷	8×	
70×							120×
2÷		2÷		210×			
	24×				35×		6
168×		120×	4÷	48×		3÷	7÷

234

543

× ÷

120×		72×	5÷		112×	
3÷			56×	140×	36×	
	3÷	80×				2÷
8		42×	240×		48×	
112×						
210×		2÷	12×		240×	
	2÷	3÷		2÷		35×
		112×				

544

× ÷

48×	140×		18×		168×	2÷
		2÷	48×			280×
	3					15×
105×	240×			2÷		
	15×	2÷		84×		2÷
			21×		2÷	126×
48×	4÷			40×	120×	
		7÷				

545

40×		336×	12×			28×	6÷
4÷			105×				
	2÷			2÷	144×		35×
105×	2÷	180×					
			56×		15×	4÷	
	168×			2÷		120×	
36×		32×					3
		210×			2÷		

546

168×		80×	2÷		48×	210×	
	30×			84×			24×
20×		56×				8÷	
		2÷	72×		252×		
	2÷						40×
126×		336×			5	2÷	
		90×		4÷			
4÷			5÷		84×		

547

× ÷

90×	224×		8	36×	2÷		280×
					4÷		
21×			60×	60×		192×	
2÷					126×		
2÷		70×					2÷
4÷	126×		4÷		150×		
	30×		56×		168×		12×
		2÷					

548

× ÷

2÷	70×			6	105×	8÷
	24×	3÷				3÷
		56×		2÷	30×	120×
42×	56×	30×			2÷	
				24×		56×
	36×	60×				
15×				7÷	180×	112×
		2÷				

549

× ÷

4÷		2÷	3÷	3÷		350×	
672×			720×				
120×		84×			2÷		
	24×			28×		336×	
		30×					
108×	140×		280×	2÷			
		120×				36×	
56×				2÷			

550

× ÷

8×		630×	315×			336×	
2÷	24×			160×			
					4÷		
960×	210×			126×			
1260×		2÷	2÷	2÷			
				240×			
	1176×	2÷	576×				
					5÷		

238

551

× ÷

280×		36×			240×	3÷	
2÷							294×
280×				540×	8÷		
2÷	5÷				336×		
	168×						
3÷	1440×		84×	480×			
	336×					80×	
		2÷					

552

× ÷

288×		1260×			12×	2÷	
	40×	280×	4÷				
60×						630×	
	8÷	882×	2÷				
2÷			48×		280×		
		3÷				360×	
210×	2÷	168×					
				64×			

239

553

× ÷

2÷	96×			112×		630×	
	315×				48×		
160×	4÷					280×	672×
		120×					
	3÷			216×			
168×	8÷		336×			200×	
		420×	3÷				2÷

554

× ÷

480×	420×			192×			168×
					168×		
840×		48×		5÷			
7÷						480×	
	6÷		2÷		5×	360×	
2÷	720×	112×					
				63×	336×		
8÷							

555

140×			280×		216×		
24×		4÷				120×	
42×		504×	2÷				
	2÷			5÷	896×		
		72×			1260×		
			1400×			4÷	
240×			168×				2÷
		72×					

556

2:	56×	504×	168×			120×	
			2÷	240×			240×
480×							
			6÷			126×	
	840×			7÷		3÷	
		150×	8÷		56×		2÷
96×				45×			
					224×		

241

557

× ÷

2940×			3÷		160×	2÷	
			3÷				3×
4÷		60×		210×			
2÷			128×		42×	70×	
24×	2÷					48×	
	40320×				72×		
						210×	
28×			40×		2÷		

558

× ÷

3÷		98×	160×			72×	5÷
28×			30×				
		120×			12544×		24×
2÷			2÷				
40×	86016×			2÷			
					5÷	72×	
30240×						140×	

242

559

×÷

56×		48×		48×	25200×		
1260×		2÷				160×	2÷
	840×	320×					
8÷					16128×		
	12×	42×				7÷	
120×			35×				
2÷					2÷		

560

×÷

24×		112×		88200×	7÷	5÷	
2÷	2÷						
48×	60×						
1960×	17280×		8×		2÷		
				4÷	54×		
15×		1960×		96×			
			24×				

243

561

× ÷

15120×				320×			7÷
56×	24×			2÷			
				2÷	120×		
12×			9216×	15×	28×		
10×					126×	2÷	
	280×			8×			
60×				210×	24×		
	7÷					4÷	

562

× ÷

3÷	4÷		210×	2240×	24×		
	210×						
			40320×		2÷		105×
4÷		45×		3÷			
448×							16128×
		2÷		45×			
10080×							
		8×					

244

563

×÷

24×		3÷		30×	28×	168×	
24×		280×	40×				1680×
						3÷	
42×			4÷	120×			
	2÷				720×		
120×	280×	18×					
			14×	168×			
					2÷	24×	

564

×÷

768×	23040×					105×	105×
			48×				
	1890×				112×		
35×						2÷	
	168×			15×		288×	8÷
		280×					
24×			2÷			2÷	
		70×				2÷	

× ÷

448×		12×		16×	225×	
	3÷	5040×			42×	
2÷				42000×		32×
	13440×		3÷		56×	
						84×
					48×	
2÷	8×					24×
	35×			48×		

× ÷

16×		336×	30×		30240×		
			5×				
84×		39690×	160×				
	16×			2÷	2÷		
40×			84×		24×		
					2÷		
30×		2÷	6×			245×	
	6÷		96×				

246

567

× ÷

46080×					7×	84×
30×	16×		3150×			24×
					192×	2÷
			7÷			
8064×				40×		2÷
56×				336×	9600×	35×
2÷		4÷				

568

× ÷

50400×			240×		9408×	
48×						
120×			24×	2÷		
		2÷			336×	90×
112×					13824×	
	3÷		245×			
63×	80×					2÷
			20×			

247

569

×÷

16128×	1260×				6÷	
	2÷	120×		7÷	40×	56×
		120×				
			7÷	128×		
	90×				48×	
	14×	192×	40×		7÷	
40×	16×					7560×

570

×÷

1344×		16×	30×	21×	6÷	40×
	12×					
		210×		2÷		
		47040×		96×		
50×					126×	
		2÷		240×	28×	
2÷	2÷	112×				
				2÷	15×	

571

$+ \ - \ \times \ \div$

80×		16×	13+	4−		3÷	
					8	3−	
7÷	40×		5−	3÷		11+	
	54×			7+	2÷		40×
5		3−			1−		
14+			13+			2−	
10+		3−			20+	2÷	2−
	15+						

572

$+ \ - \ \times \ \div$

3÷	4÷	2−		12+		2÷	
		1−		4−		8+	
448×		1−			12+		
	28×			18+		24×	
30×		2÷	4−			12+	
4−			6÷	14×			6
	13+	16+			2−	12+	1−

573

+ − × ÷

42×			5	10+	2−	7÷
9+		112×			12+	14+
	3−					2−
3−	63×	4÷	5−			
			6÷	4−	5−	2−
15+	144×	5÷				
	9+		16+	10+	2÷	
				28×		

574

+ − × ÷

5÷	6−		4−	15+	4÷	15+
	17+					
12+	3−		14+	2÷	50×	6×
		24×				
			5÷	35×	1	192×
2−	2÷				4−	
	10+	4−	9+		8+	2−
					2−	

575

20×	12+			3÷	15+	17+
	7÷		10+		192×	
3−				96×		
21×	8	2−	15+		1−	150×
						6÷
1−		3−		15+	16+	
2−	8÷				2÷	9+
	1−		1−			

576

11+		3−		1−	15+	3−
	112×		20+			4÷
2−	2÷			2−		18+
		3		1−		64×
15+		12+			14+	1−
	144×	2−	4÷			
				112×	7÷	
3−		2÷			10+	

251

577

$+ - \times \div$

13+		8+	5−	17+		48×
				2−		
15+	49×		14+		72×	3+
			60×		6÷	
13+				1−		1−
4−		12+		5÷	5	
1−	2÷		7÷		3÷	
	6×			2−		2−

578

$+ - \times \div$

9+			168×	23+		2−
2−		3−				2−
13+			48×		45×	6
	9+			16+		8÷
2−	2÷		3−			7÷
	16+			3−		4÷
5−	15+		8+		56×	120×
			2÷			

579

$+ \; - \; \times \; \div$

49×		23+	288×	2÷	8+
2÷		8+		2−	
			9+	3−	672×
30×	2−	147×			
672×				2−	
		7−	75×		
1−	19+	7÷		14+	
			2÷		

580

$+ \; - \; \times \; :$

4+	2−	15+	896×	3−
21+			2÷	
	2÷		12×	2÷
2÷	24+	560×	5−	
			252×	120×
	5+	2−	3	
60×			336×	13+
	4−			5−

253

581

+ − × ÷

5−	224×		315×	18+			15×
		3−				252×	
3−			12+				
	3÷			4÷	3÷		784×
2÷	840×	4+			1−		
				11+			
24+			30×		1−		13+
				4−			

582

+ − × ÷

3−	4−	8+		15+		80×	
		8		26+			
3−	8÷				10+		
	240×	3−	12+		3÷		6÷
				288×		140×	
	4÷						480×
36×		56×					
		11+		3−		1−	

583

+ − × ÷

15+	360×			6÷		5−
		210×		4−		4−
	224×			21+	17+	
				2÷		
13+		8+	3−			21+
40×	4×		2÷		432×	
		245×				
	1−			1−	4÷	

584

+ − × ÷

1−		20+	168×		5−		1344×
3÷			320×				
				14+			4−
4÷		252×			2−	576×	
1−	7÷						
		19+		25+	7+		
19+	8÷					17+	
			2−				

585

+ − × ÷

7−		2−		15+	25+		4−
8+		2−					
11+	25+			64×		8÷
				23+		
768×	1−	11+		320×		
		160×	3÷		1−	
			7÷			12+
2−		6÷				

586

+ − × ÷

13+		42×			2÷	
14+	1−		3−	4−	4+	
	120×			336×	21+
	1568×				
2÷	252×		6÷	2−	
	13+		360×		
2−	11+		5÷		
		40×		4−	

256

587

$+ - \times \div$

2÷	2−		18×		6÷		280×
	27+				240×		
1−							126×
6÷		4480×				2÷	
14+			14×		72×		
		2−	1				2−
		96×	280×				
42×					14+		

588

$+ - \times \div$

15+	128×		14+			2880×	
		48×		3÷			
	40×		2÷		28×		
		4320×			8820×		
4×						33+	
		196×	5−				
2÷						1−	
280×			2−		2÷		

+ − × ÷

56×	5−	15+		245×		2−
		4×			480×	
	22+	35×	11+			8÷
				2	27+	
	13+	24+				
	2÷					2940×
5−			240×			
	21×			4÷		

+ − × ÷

2÷		1−		7560×	3−		3−
3÷	48×					14×	
	5÷				11+		
2520×		28×				128×	
35×		16×	4−			12+	
	7+						126×
	5−	14+					
2−			2÷		18+		

591

$+ - \times \div$

24×		37800×		33+			
	1−			4−			
4÷				14×			
	126×	1−		4−	92160×		30×
4−		4×					
	128×						7×
2÷		14×			4		
12+		2÷		5+		6÷	

592

$+ - \times \div$

4÷	3−		90720×				
	4÷			14+	3×		
16×	20+	12+			6−		
			128×	11+	2−		
					12+	10×	
2−		12+	18×		6÷		
2÷			3840×		22+		

259

593

+ − × ÷

15+			8×		10×	26+	
75×		6−		36×		20+	
3−							
	2÷	26+			4032×		
3÷		1−					
	35×		9408×			6÷	
3	15+		1−				
2÷					10×		

594

+ − × ÷

2×		1−	35×		140×	2−	
10×			336×			44100×	2÷
	37+			48×			
	7056×						
		10+		2÷		2−	
	8	240×		4÷	240×		3÷

260

595

+ − × ÷

6	56×		18000×		27+	2−
24192×						
				2÷		35×
	336×					
3−	6÷			30×	38+	
	400×					5−
	18×	98×				
2÷						

596

+ − × ÷

16+		70560×			24×
		33+	150×		
24+	14×			10+	
		2÷			
	50×	20160×			
1−	8+				
3−		2÷	2÷	6×	
3	1−				

597

+ − × ÷

3−	16+		24+	17+
50400×				
	24×	4÷	7680×	
		3780×		
32×	40×	48×	1−	72×	5÷
	3−			16+	
	14×	4÷			

598

+ − × ÷

11+	22+	6−	4200×	5
2÷				2÷
26+		67200×		
	3−	15+		56×
			288×	
				18+
84×		5÷	32×	2−
40×				10+

262

599

+ − × ÷

28+					300×	7÷
6300×		2−				
		896×		70560×		
192×						11+
		12+				
30×		2−				
7÷	168×			2−	32+	
		5÷				

600

+ − × ÷

3−	2304×		2÷	5÷	40320×		270×
		15+					
			7×				
	1080×				13+		
40×	2−	26+				1−	
							10752×
				1−			
7+		5÷					

1

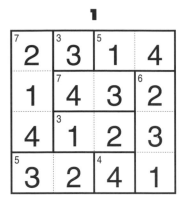

2

3

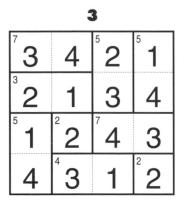

4

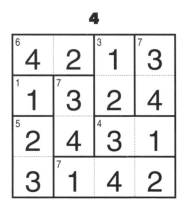

5

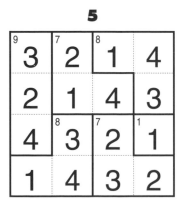

6

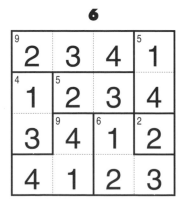

7

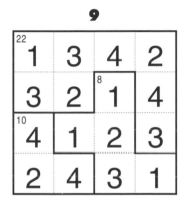

2	4	1	3
3	2	4	1
4	1	3	2
1	3	2	4

8

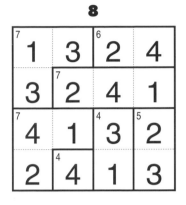

1	3	2	4
3	2	4	1
4	1	3	2
2	4	1	3

9

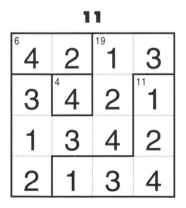

1	3	4	2
3	2	1	4
4	1	2	3
2	4	3	1

10

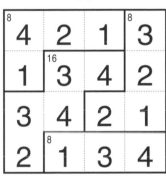

4	2	1	3
1	3	4	2
3	4	2	1
2	1	3	4

11

4	2	1	3
3	4	2	1
1	3	4	2
2	1	3	4

12

1	3	2	4
3	4	1	2
2	1	4	3
4	2	3	1

13

21		9	
1	4	2	3
4	1	3	2 (8)
3	2	4	1
2 (2)	3	1	4

14

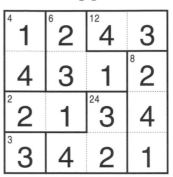

4	6	12	
1	2	4	3
4	3	1	2 (8)
2 (2)	1	3 (24)	4
3 (3)	4	2	1

15

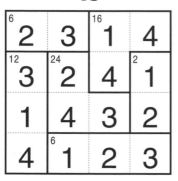

6		16	
2	3	1	4
3 (12)	2 (24)	4	1 (2)
1	4	3	2
4	1 (6)	2	3

16

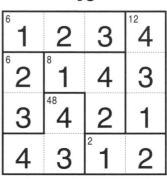

6			12
1	2	3	4
2 (6)	1 (8)	4	3
3	4 (48)	2	1
4	3	1 (2)	2

17

8	3		24
4	3	1	2
1	2	4 (8)	3
3 (6)	1	2	4
2	4 (12)	3	1

18

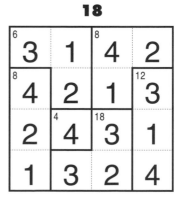

6		8	
3	1	4	2
4 (8)	2	1	3 (12)
2	4 (4)	3 (18)	1
1	3	2	4

19

8 1	12 3	2	12 4
4	2	1	3
2	12 4	12 3	2 1
3	1	4	2

20

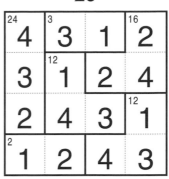

24 4	3 3	1	16 2
3	12 1	2	4
2	4	3	12 1
2 1	2	4	3

21

24 3	4	2	3 1
16 4	2	3 1	3
2	1	3	32 4
3 1	3	4	2

22

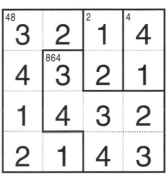

48 3	2	2 1	4 4
4	864 3	2	1
1	4	3	2
2	1	4	3

23

16 4	48 1	2	3
1	4	24 3	2
18 2	3	1	4
3	2	4	1

24

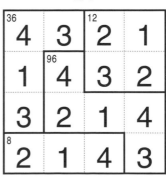

36 4	3	12 2	1
1	96 4	3	2
3	2	1	4
8 2	1	4	3

³²4	¹⁸1	3	2
2	3	¹²1	4
1	4	⁴⁸2	3
3	2	4	1

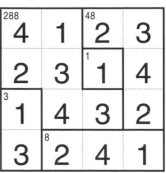

²⁸⁸4	1	⁴⁸2	3
2	3	¹1	4
³1	4	3	2
3	⁸2	4	1

3−4	1−2	1	6+3
1	⁴4	1−3	2
1−2	3	4	1
4+3	1	6+2	4

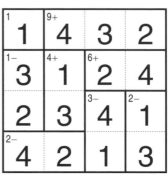

¹1	9+4	3	2
1−3	4+1	6+2	4
2	3	3−4	2−1
2−4	2	1	3

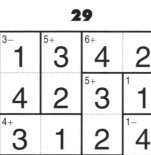

3−1	5+3	6+4	2
4	2	5+3	¹1
4+3	1	2	1−4
7+2	4	1	3

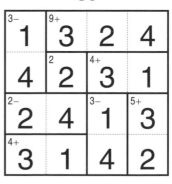

3−1	9+3	2	4
4	²2	4+3	1
2−2	4	3−1	5+3
4+3	1	4	2

31

³ 1-	4	¹ 7+	2
² 7+	¹ 4+	3	4
1	² 7+	⁴ 1-	3
4	3	2	¹ 1

32

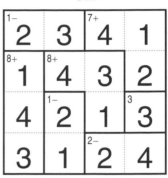

33

² 1-	³ 8+	1	4
3	² 6+	⁴ 4	¹ 1-
¹ 6+	4	³ 8+	2
4	1	2	3

34

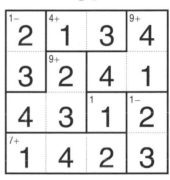

35

³ 1-	⁴ 10+	2	1
4	2	1	³ 12+
¹ 4+	³ 1-	4	2
2	1	3	4

36

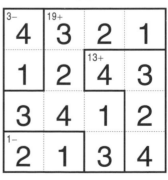

269

14+ 4	3	1	2
2	1	14+ 3	1− 4
1	4	2	3
3	2	3− 4	1

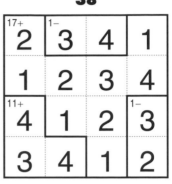

17+ 2	1− 3	4	1
1	2	3	4
11+ 4	1	2	1− 3
3	4	1	2

1− 2	29+ 3	3− 1	4
1	4	3	3+ 2
3	2	4	1
4	1	2	3

2	12× 3	2÷ 4	4÷ 1
12× 3	1	2	4
1	4	6× 3	2
4	6× 2	1	3

3× 3	8× 2	4	1
1	6× 3	2	4 4
2÷ 4	4÷ 1	6× 3	2
2	4	3× 1	3

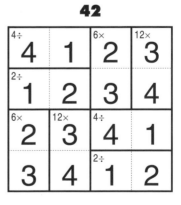

4÷ 4	1	6× 2	12× 3
2÷ 1	2	3	4
6× 2	12× 3	4÷ 4	1
3	4	2÷ 1	2

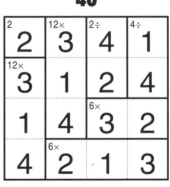

43

4 (12×)	3 (6×)	1	2
1	2 (2÷)	4	3 (12×)
3	1 (2×)	2	4
2 (2÷)	4	3 (3÷)	1

44

3 (6×)	2	4 (4÷)	1
2 (2÷)	3 (6×)	1	4 (24×)
4	1 (12×)	2	3
1 (1)	4	3	2

45

3 (6×)	1 (2÷)	2	4 (12×)
2	4 (2÷)	1	3
4 (12×)	2	3 (12×)	1 (2÷)
1	3	4	2

46

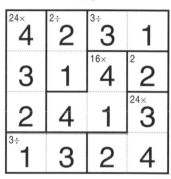

4 (24×)	2 (2÷)	3 (3÷)	1
3	1	4 (16×)	2 (2)
2	4	1	3 (24×)
1 (3÷)	3	2	4

47

3 (3×)	2 (2÷)	1	4 (24×)
1	4 (4)	3	2
4 (24×)	3	2 (2÷)	1
2	1 (12×)	4	3

48

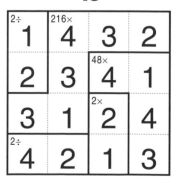

1 (2÷)	4 (216×)	3	2
2	3	4 (48×)	1
3	1	2 (2×)	4
4 (2÷)	2	1	3

49

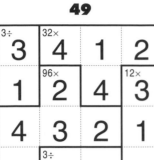

3 (3÷)	4 (32×)	1	2
1	2 (96×)	4	3 (12×)
4	3	2	1
2	1 (3÷)	3	4

50

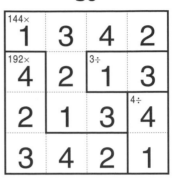

1 (144×)	3	4	2
4 (192×)	2	1 (3÷)	3
2	1	3	4 (4÷)
3	4	2	1

51

2 (6×)	1 (12×)	3	4 (4÷)
3	2 (576×)	4	1
1	4	2	3
4	3	1 (2÷)	2

52

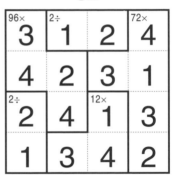

3 (96×)	1 (2÷)	2	4 (72×)
4	2	3	1
2 (2÷)	4	1 (12×)	3
1	3	4	2

53

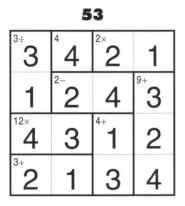

3 (3÷)	4 (4)	2 (2×)	1
1	2 (2−)	4	3 (9+)
4 (12×)	3	1 (4+)	2
2 (3+)	1	3	4

54

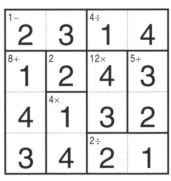

2 (1−)	3	1 (4÷)	4
1 (8+)	2 (2)	4 (12×)	3 (5+)
4	1 (4×)	3	2
3	4	2 (2÷)	1

55

4	1−		7+
4	1	2	3
2÷ 1	2	8+ 3	4
12× 3	4	1	1− 2
5+ 2	3	4	1

56

2− 2	4+ 3	4÷ 1	4
4	1	9+ 3	2 2
3− 1	4	2	3× 3
5+ 3	2	4	1

57

1− 2	3	9+ 1	4
12× 3	2 2	4	2÷ 1
4	2− 1	3	2
5+ 1	4	6× 2	3

58

2÷ 1	2	8+ 4	3
1− 3	2− 4	2	1
2	7+ 3	1	2÷ 4
4× 4	1	3	2

59

1− 4	2÷ 1	6× 2	3
3	2	6+ 4	1
5+ 2	3	1	2÷ 4
8+ 1	4	3	2

60

9+ 2	2− 1	3	8+ 4
4	3	2÷ 2	1
3× 1	2÷ 2	4	3
3	4	1− 1	2

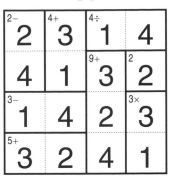
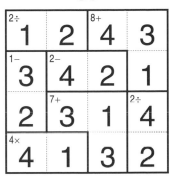
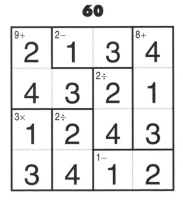

61

¹⁻ 1	²÷ 2	¹²ˣ 4	3
2	4	⁸⁺ 3	1
³ˣ 3	1	⁵⁺ 2	4
¹⁻ 4	3	1	2

62

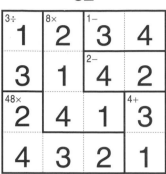

³÷ 1	⁸ˣ 2	¹⁻ 3	4
3	1	²⁻ 4	2
⁴⁸ˣ 2	4	1	⁴⁺ 3
4	3	2	1

63

³⁶ˣ 3	4	¹¹⁺ 1	²÷ 2
¹⁻ 1	3	2	4
2	²⁴ˣ 1	4	3
4	2	3	1

64

¹⁻ 4	3	⁹⁺ 1	²÷ 2
⁷⁺ 3	1	2	4
1	2	4	³⁶ˣ 3
2	4	3	1

65

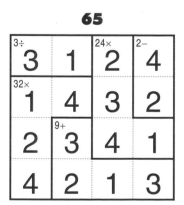

³÷ 3	1	²⁴ˣ 2	²⁻ 4
³²ˣ 1	4	3	2
2	⁹⁺ 3	4	1
4	2	1	3

66

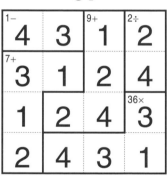

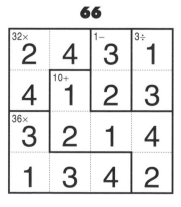

³²ˣ 2	4	¹⁻ 3	³÷ 1
4	¹⁰⁺ 1	2	3
³⁶ˣ 3	2	1	4
1	3	4	2

67

5	2	3	4	1
3	1	4	2	5
2	4	1	5	3
4	3	5	1	2
1	5	2	3	4

68

3	2	5	4	1
2	4	3	1	5
1	5	2	3	4
4	3	1	5	2
5	1	4	2	3

69

4	3	2	1	5
2	1	3	5	4
1	5	4	2	3
3	2	5	4	1
5	4	1	3	2

70

3	1	5	4	2
1	4	2	5	3
4	5	3	2	1
2	3	4	1	5
5	2	1	3	4

71

1	2	3	5	4
3	5	1	4	2
2	4	5	3	1
4	3	2	1	5
5	1	4	2	3

72

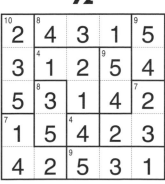

2	4	3	1	5
3	1	2	5	4
5	3	1	4	2
1	5	4	2	3
4	2	5	3	1

73

¹¹2	4	³1	⁸5	3
¹1	5	2	⁷3	4
¹²4	⁵2	3	⁷1	⁸5
5	⁴3	4	2	1
3	1	⁹5	4	2

74

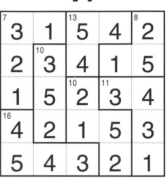

⁷3	1	¹³5	4	⁸2
2	¹⁰3	4	1	5
1	5	¹⁰2	¹¹3	4
¹⁶4	2	1	5	3
5	4	3	2	1

75

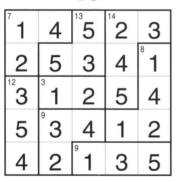

⁷1	4	¹³5	¹⁴2	3
2	5	3	4	⁸1
¹²3	³1	2	5	4
5	⁹3	4	1	2
4	2	⁹1	3	5

76

¹²2	¹²5	1	3	¹¹4
1	4	3	5	2
5	⁸1	2	¹²4	3
⁷3	2	⁹4	⁴1	5
4	3	5	2	1

77

⁸3	¹¹2	4	5	⁸1
4	1	¹¹5	3	2
³1	¹⁷4	3	¹³2	5
2	5	⁴1	4	3
5	3	2	1	4

78

⁷1	4	¹³2	3	5
2	²¹3	4	5	1
¹²3	5	⁵1	4	2
5	1	3	⁹2	4
4	⁸2	5	1	3

79

ⁱ⁹4	3	¹⁰1	2	5
¹⁵1	5	3	4	2
5	4	⁵2	3	⁹1
2	³1	¹⁴4	5	3
3	2	5	1	4

80

⁸3	1	2	¹⁴5	⁵4
2	²¹3	5	4	1
5	4	¹³1	2	3
⁷1	5	4	⁷3	2
4	2	3	1	5

81

⁸1	²¹5	4	⁶3	2
5	2	3	4	1
⁵2	¹¹3	5	1	¹⁷4
3	4	1	2	5
⁷4	1	2	5	3

82

¹⁰3	5	³1	2	⁸4
⁷4	2	¹¹5	1	3
2	²⁵3	4	¹¹5	1
1	4	2	3	5
5	1	3	4	2

83

⁷3	4	¹³2	5	⁸1
4	1	3	2	³²5
1	2	5	4	3
2	5	⁹1	3	⁶4
5	3	4	1	2

84

⁹2	³⁵5	3	4	⁴1
1	2	4	5	3
¹⁶5	3	1	2	4
4	1	5	⁵3	2
3	4	2	⁶1	5

85

2	12	20		5
2	3	4	5	1
1	4	[6] 3	2	5
[5] 5	1	[2] 2	[12] 4	[6] 3
[20] 4	5	[5] 1	3	2
[6] 3	2	5	[4] 1	4

86

15		10	4	
5	3	2	1	4
[3] 1	[8] 4	5	[6] 2	3
3	2	[20] 4	5	[1] 1
[2] 2	1	[3] 3	[12] 4	[10] 5
[20] 4	5	1	3	2

87

3	20	2	4	
3	5	2	4	1
1	4	[15] 5	[6] 3	2
[5] 5	1	3	[2] 2	[20] 4
[8] 2	[12] 3	4	1	5
4	[2] 2	1	[15] 5	3

88

20			6	2
5	4	1	3	2
[40] 2	5	4	1	[12] 3
[12] 4	[15] 3	5	2	1
3	[2] 1	[10] 2	5	4
1	2	[60] 3	4	5

89

3	40		6	
3	2	5	4	1
[40] 2	5	4	[5] 1	3
[20] 4	[12] 3	[2] 1	5	2
5	1	2	[12] 3	4
1	4	[30] 3	2	5

90

6			15	40
2	3	1	5	4
[15] 1	[8] 2	4	3	5
3	[20] 4	5	1	2
5	[1] 1	[24] 2	4	3
[60] 4	5	3	[2] 2	1

91

30		20	6	
5	3	4	1	2
2	5	1	3	20 4
48 4	3 1	3	20 2	5
3	4	2	5	1
2 1	2	60 5	4	3

92

8	5		12	
2	5	1	3	4
4	30 3	5	2	1
1	12 4	3	50 5	2
30 3	1	8 2	12 4	5
5	2	4	1	3

93

20		12	15	
2	5	4	1	3
20 4	2	1	3	5
5	12 4	30 3	2	2 1
1	3	5	80 4	2
6 3	1	2	5	4

94

20	3		60	6
4	1	3	5	2
1	5	40 2	4	3
12 2	4	5	3	1
3	2	8 4	20 1	5
15 5	3	1	2	4

95

30	240			
2	4	5	1	3
3	5	1	40 2	4
1	40 2	36 3	4	5
5	1	4	3	60 2
4	3	2	5	1

96

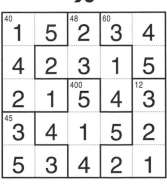

40		48	60	
1	5	2	3	4
4	2	3	1	5
2	1	400 5	4	12 3
45 3	4	1	5	2
5	3	4	2	1

97

60			240	
3	1	4	2	5
5	60 3	2	4	24 1
2	5	300 1	3	4
4 4	2	5	1	3
1	4	3	5	2

98

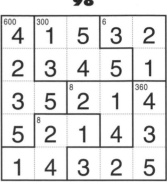

600	300		6	
4	1	5	3	2
2	3	4	5	1
3	5	8 2	1	360 4
5	8 2	1	4	3
1	4	3	2	5

99

9000			15	
2	4	1	3	5
5	720 2	3	8 1	4
3	1	4	5	2
4 4	3	5	2	1
1	5	8 2	4	3

100

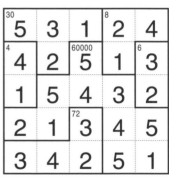

30			8	
5	3	1	2	4
4 4	2	60000 5	1	6 3
1	5	4	3	2
2	1	72 3	4	5
3	4	2	5	1

101

96			100	
3	1	4	2	5
2	4	2160 3	5	1
300 5	3	1	4	2
4 1	2	5	3	4
4	5	2	1	3

102

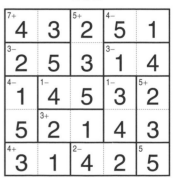

7+		5+	4−	
4	3	2	5	1
3− 2	5	3	3− 1	4
4− 1	1− 4	5	1− 3	5+ 2
5	3+ 2	1	4	3
4+ 3	1	2− 4	2	5 5

280

103

1 (3−)	4 (2−)	2	5 (8+)	3
4	2 (5+)	1 (4+)	3	5 (4−)
2 (7+)	3	5 (1−)	4	1
5	1 (4+)	3	2 (2)	4 (6+)
3 (2−)	5	4 (3−)	1	2

104

3 (8+)	5 (4−)	1	4 (4)	2 (6+)
5	1 (2−)	3	2 (3−)	4
2 (1−)	3 (7+)	4 (4)	5	1 (4−)
1	4	2 (5+)	3	5
4 (4)	2 (7+)	5	1 (2−)	3

105

2 (5+)	5 (12+)	3 (8+)	4	1
3	4	2 (1−)	1 (4−)	5
5 (1−)	3	1	2 (2−)	4
4	1 (9+)	5	3	2 (5+)
1 (7+)	2	4	5 (5)	3

106

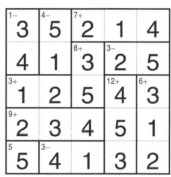

3 (1−)	5 (4−)	2 (7+)	1	4
4	1	3 (8+)	2 (3−)	5
1 (3+)	2	5	4 (12+)	3 (6+)
2 (9+)	3	4	5	1
5 (5)	4 (3−)	1	3	2

107

1 (10+)	4 (1−)	3	2 (6+)	5 (3−)
5	3 (6+)	1 (4−)	4	2
4	2	5	3 (4+)	1
3 (1−)	1	2 (11+)	5	4
2	5 (10+)	4	1	3 (3)

108

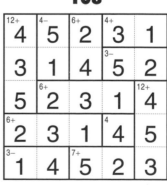

4 (12+)	5 (4−)	2 (6+)	3 (4+)	1
3	1	4	5 (3−)	2
5	2 (6+)	3	1	4 (12+)
2 (6+)	3	1	4 (4)	5
1 (3−)	4	5 (7+)	2	3

109

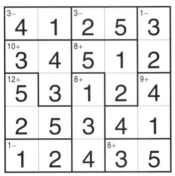

2⁹⁺	5²⁻	3	4⁵⁺	1
3	4	2⁴⁺	1	5²⁻
4¹⁰⁺	2¹⁻	1	5³⁻	3
1	3	5¹⁰⁺	2	4⁹⁺
5	1	4	3	2

110

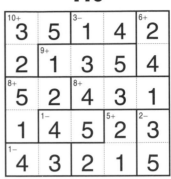

3¹⁰⁺	5	1³⁻	4	2⁶⁺
2	1⁹⁺	3	5	4
5⁸⁺	2	4⁸⁺	3	1
1	4¹⁻	5	2⁵⁺	3²⁻
4¹⁻	3	2	1	5

111

4³⁻	1	2³⁻	5	3¹⁻
3¹⁰⁺	4	5⁸⁺	1	2
5¹²⁺	3	1⁸⁺	2	4⁹⁺
2	5	3	4	1
1¹⁻	2	4	3⁸⁺	5

112

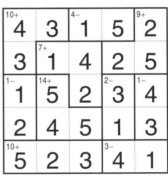

4¹⁰⁺	3	1⁴⁻	5	2⁹⁺
3	1⁷⁺	4	2	5
1¹⁻	5¹⁴⁺	2	3²⁻	4¹⁻
2	4	5	1	3
5¹⁰⁺	2	3	4³⁻	1

113

5¹⁵⁺	1³⁻	4	2¹⁻	3
1	2	3	5¹⁴⁺	4
3¹⁻	4	2⁷⁺	1	5
4	5¹⁹⁺	1	3	2¹⁻
2	3	5	4	1

114

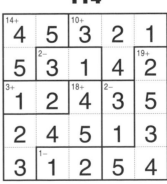

4¹⁴⁺	5	3¹⁰⁺	2	1
5	3²⁻	1	4	2¹⁹⁺
1³⁺	2	4¹⁸⁺	3²⁻	5
2	4	5	1	3
3	1¹⁻	2	5	4

115

11+ 3	5	2- 2	4	11+ 1
1- 2	3	21+ 5	1	4
1	4	3	5	2
9+ 5	1- 1	4	11+ 2	3
4	2	1	3	5

116

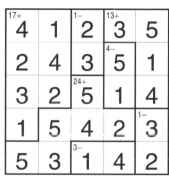

7+ 2	4	6+ 1	17+ 5	3
3- 4	1	2	3	5
1	8+ 5	3	1- 2	4
21+ 5	3	4	1	1- 2
1- 3	2	5	4	1

117

12+ 1	2	4	13+ 5	3
3	24+ 4	2	1	5
3- 2	5	3	4	3- 1
5	8+ 3	4+ 1	2	4
4	1	5	3	2

118

17+ 4	1	1- 2	13+ 3	5
2	4	3	4- 5	1
3	2	24+ 5	1	4
1	5	4	2	1- 3
5	3	3- 1	4	2

119

1- 1	6+ 2	31+ 3	5	4
2	4	5	11+ 1	2- 3
3	5	4	2	1
10+ 4	1	2	3	5
5	2- 3	1	2- 4	2

120

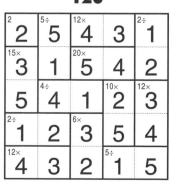

2 2	5÷ 5	12× 4	3	2÷ 1
15× 3	1	20× 5	4	2
5	4÷ 4	1	10× 2	12× 3
2÷ 1	2	6× 3	5	4
12× 4	3	2	5÷ 1	5

121

6×	3÷		4×	20×
2	3	1	4	5
3	5 (10×)	2	1	4
1 (5÷)	2 (8×)	4 (20×)	5	3 (3÷)
5	4	3 (15×)	2 (2)	1
4 (4÷)	1	5	3 (6×)	2

122

20×		8×	3÷	
5	4	2	3	1
2 (10×)	5	4	1 (5÷)	3 (6×)
4 (4)	1 (3÷)	3	5	2
3 (3÷)	2 (6×)	1 (4÷)	4	5 (20×)
1	3	5 (10×)	2	4

123

15×	60×			10×
1	5	3	4	2
3	1 (8×)	4	2	5
5	4 (2÷)	2	3 (3÷)	1 (4÷)
2 (2÷)	3 (6×)	5 (5)	1	4
4	2	1 (15×)	5	3

124

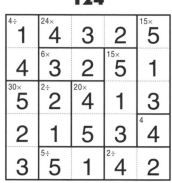

4÷	24×			15×
1	4	3	2	5
4	3 (6×)	2	5 (15×)	1
5 (30×)	2 (2÷)	4 (20×)	1	3
2	1	5	3	4 (4)
3	5 (5÷)	1	4 (2÷)	2

125

15×		2÷	4÷	2
5	3	4	1	2
3 (24×)	5 (5÷)	2	4	1 (12×)
2	1	5 (15×)	3	4
4	2 (10×)	1	5	3
1 (4÷)	4	3 (30×)	2	5

126

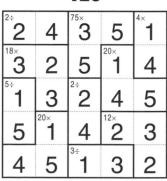

2÷		75×		4×
2	4	3	5	1
3 (18×)	2	5	1 (20×)	4
1 (5÷)	3	2 (2÷)	4	5
5	1 (20×)	4	2 (12×)	3
4	5	1 (3÷)	3	2

127

60×		2÷		5÷
5	3	4	2	1
4	4÷ 1	18× 2	3	5
2÷ 1	4	3	10× 5	2
2	30× 5	20× 1	4	12× 3
3	2	5	1	4

128

5÷	2÷		15×	
1	4	2	3	5
5	4÷ 1	4	30× 2	3
12× 4	3	1	5	2÷ 2
12× 2	75× 5	3	16× 4	1
3	2	5	1	4

129

15×		2÷	2÷	
3	5	4	1	2
30× 5	1	2	12× 3	4
2	3	20× 5	4	1
4: 4	2: 2	1	30× 5	15× 3
1	4	3	2	5

130

90×			4×	
5	2	3	1	4
3	300× 5	2÷ 2	4	12× 1
1	4	5	3	2
2÷ 4	3	1	2	75× 5
2	4÷ 1	4	5	3

131

2÷	3÷		500×	
2	3	1	4	5
4	2÷ 2	5	1	3÷ 3
15× 3	4	240× 2	5	1
5	1	4	24× 3	2
1	5	3	2	4

132

2÷	3÷	300×		
2	1	5	3	4
4	3	6× 2	4× 1	5
60× 5	4	3	2	1
3	300× 5	1	4	2
1	2÷ 2	4	5	3

2÷ 1	2	240× 5	4	6× 3
3	1	4	300× 5	2
2÷ 2	5	1	3	4
4	60× 3	12× 2	5÷ 1	5
5	4	3	2	1

2÷ 2	1	240× 4	3	5
18000× 3	120× 2	5	4	1
4	5	2	1	3
5	3÷ 3	1	2	2÷ 4
1	4	3	5	2

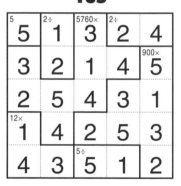

5 5	2÷ 1	5760× 3	2÷ 2	4
3	2	1	4	900× 5
2	5	4	3	1
12× 1	4	2	5	3
4	3	5÷ 5	1	2

2÷ 4	2	300× 3	5	1
2880× 2	3	4	1	5
60× 1	5	2	4	3
3	1	10× 5	2	4
5	4	3÷ 1	3	2 2

5+ 3	2	20× 4	6+ 5	1
8× 2	2− 1	5	3− 4	15× 3
4	3	2÷ 2	1	5
9+ 5	4	1	1− 3	2
5÷ 1	5	3 3	2÷ 2	4

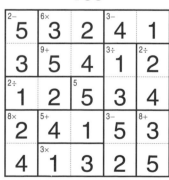

2− 5	6× 3	2	3− 4	1
3	9+ 5	4	3÷ 1	2÷ 2
2÷ 1	2	5 5	3	4
8× 2	5+ 4	1	3− 5	8+ 3
4	1	3× 3	2	5

139

2÷ 2	2− 5	3	4× 1	4
4	3+ 1	2	1− 3	15× 5
6+ 1	1− 4	5	2	3
5	5+ 3	4÷ 1	8× 4	2
3 3	2	4	5÷ 5	1

140

2÷ 1	11+ 5	12× 4	6× 3	2
2	4	3	5÷ 1	5
3 3	2	4− 1	5	8+ 4
12+ 4	3	5	2− 2	1
8+ 5	1	2	4	3

141

3− 4	1	15× 5	2÷ 2	2− 3
6+ 5	2 2	3	4	1
1	12+ 5	9+ 2	3	4
6× 2	3	10+ 4	1	5
3	4	5÷ 1	5	2 2

142

3− 5	2	4÷ 1	2÷ 4	10+ 3
3× 3	1	4	2	5
7+ 4	9+ 5	3	1	2
1	1− 3	10× 2	5	4 4
2	4	9+ 5	3	1

143

45× 3	5	15+ 1	2÷ 2	4
2÷ 2	3	4	5	1− 1
4	20× 1	5	9× 3	2
5	4	14+ 2	1	3
1− 1	2	3	4	5

144

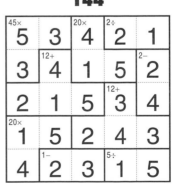

45× 5	3	20× 4	2÷ 2	1
3	12+ 4	1	5	2− 2
2	1	5	12+ 3	4
20× 1	5	2	4	3
4	1− 2	3	5÷ 1	5

145

5 ^10+	2 ^2÷	4 ^12×	1	3
4	1	3 ^1−	2	5 ^100×
1	3 ^1−	2	5	4
3 ^11+	5	1	4 ^16+	2 ^2÷
2	4	5	3	1

146

4 ^48×	2	5 ^6+	1	3 ^2−
2	5 ^21+	4	3	1
3	4 ^7+	1 ^2÷	5	2 ^3−
1 ^15×	3	2	4	5
5	1	3	2 ^2÷	4

147

1 ^3−	5 ^19+	3	4	2
4	2 ^10+	5	1 ^60×	3
2	3	4	5	1 ^5÷
3	4 ^40×	1 ^2÷	2	5
5	1	2	3 ^1−	4

148

3 ^19+	5	2 ^2÷	4	1 ^2−
5	2 ^2−	4	1 ^14+	3
2	1	5	3	4
4	3 ^36×	1 ^5÷	5	2 ^20×
1	4	3	2	5

149

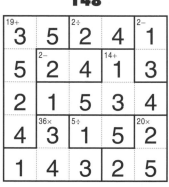

1 ^4÷	4 ^1−	2 ^240×	3	5
4	5	3 ^18+	1	2
2 ^5760×	3	1	5	4
3	2	5	4	1
5	1	4	2	3

150

1 ^5÷	5	4 ^10+	3 ^4320×	2
2 ^3−	1	5	4	3
5	3 ^1−	2 ^2÷	1	4
4 ^11+	2	3	5	1
3	4	1	2 ^10×	5

151

2	1	4	3	5	6
6	4	5	2	1	3
1	6	2	4	3	5
4	2	3	5	6	1
5	3	1	6	2	4
3	5	6	1	4	2

152

6	3	1	2	4	5
3	5	4	1	2	6
2	4	5	6	1	3
1	2	6	3	5	4
4	1	3	5	6	2
5	6	2	4	3	1

153

1	4	2	3	6	5
2	6	5	1	3	4
5	2	6	4	1	3
6	5	3	2	4	1
4	3	1	6	5	2
3	1	4	5	2	6

154

6	3	4	5	1	2
1	2	3	6	4	5
4	1	6	2	5	3
2	5	1	3	6	4
5	4	2	1	3	6
3	6	5	4	2	1

155

5	4	6	1	3	2
4	6	1	3	2	5
2	5	3	4	6	1
3	2	5	6	1	4
6	1	2	5	4	3
1	3	4	2	5	6

156

5	3	1	4	2	6
4	6	5	2	1	3
6	4	2	1	3	5
1	2	3	5	6	4
2	5	6	3	4	1
3	1	4	6	5	2

157

15	6		7	11	
4	2	3	1	5	6
6	12 5	1	4	6 3	2
5	3	4	2	11 6	1
12 1	6	5	3	2	4 4
9 3	4	9 2	12 6	1	5
2	1	6	12 5	4	3

158

5	8	9			6
3	4	1	6	2	5
2	3	12 6	12 5	4	1
16 5	1	2	4	3	8 6
6	5	4 4	8 3	6 1	2
11 1	6	3	2	5	13 4
4	8 2	5	1	6	3

159

24		7		20	
6	3	2	1	4	5
7 1	4	3	6	5	16 2
4	5	1	2	3	6
2	6	20 4	5	3 1	3
11 5	1	6	18 3	2	4
3	2	5	4	6	1

160

11				15	
5	3	2	1	6	4
12 1	23 5	4	2	3	19 6
2	6	3	5	4	1
4	2	17 5	6	10 1	3
3	12 1	6	4	2	5
6	4	1	3	7 5	2

161

16	7			13	
5	2	3	1	4	6
4	5	1	24 6	3	3 2
2	4	6	3	5	1
5 3	1	16 4	2	6	15 5
1	18 6	5	4	2	3
9 6	3	2	5	1	4

162

16			4	9	16
1	5	6	4	3	2
4	5 2	3	5	1	6
17 3	3 1	2	25 6	4	5
2	4	5	8 1	6	3
17 6	3	1	2	5	4
5	6	4	6 3	2	1

163

17	10		18		12
2	4	6	3	5	1
4	5	3	6	1	2
9 3	6	31 1	5	2	4
6	2	4	7 1	3	5
1	3	5	2	19 4	6
5	3 1	2	4	6	3

164

6		11	14		
2	1	4	3	6	5
3	37 5	1	6	8 4	2
12 6	3	5	1	2	14 4
1	10 4	6	2	5	3
5	2	3	4	4 1	6
10 4	6	2	5	3	1

165

12 3	4	5	4 1	2	10 6
14 5	6	23 2	24 4	1	3
2	3	4	5	6	1
6	2	1	3	13 5	4
1	26 5	3	6	4	2
4	1	6	2	3	5

166

7 4	2	32 5	1	6	3
8 5	1	6	3	6 2	4
3	6	2	15 5	10 4	1
8 1	3	4	6	5	8 2
16 2	5	3	4	16 1	6
6	4	1	2	3	5

167

12 2	5	10 3	4	1	24 6
1	4	2	42 5	6	3
3	6	5	2	4	1
5	8 1	6	8 3	2	4
6	2	4	1	3	7 5
4	15 3	1	6	5	2

168

3 2	1	13 4	42 6	3	6 5
10 4	5	6	3	2	1
1	6 4	2	5	6	5 3
23 6	3	5 1	4	5	2
8 3	2	5	1	4	6
5	6	5 3	2	1	4

169

11 5	11 1	42 6	3	3 2	4
6	4	6 3	2	1	5
4	2	1	6	5	3
20 3	5	2	8 1	4	6
1	6	5	9 4	3	2
9 2	3	4	5	7 6	1

170

24 6	1	3	6 2	4	7 5
5	46 6	1	4	11 3	2
1	4	5	17 3	2	6
3	5	2	6	9 1	4
6 4	2	6	1	5	3
2	3	4	5	6	1

171

30 5	2	3	24 4	6	1
4 4	1	10 2	90 6	5	3
36 2	6 6	5	10 1	12 3	4
3	4 4	1	5	8 2	60 6
6	12 3	4	2	1	5
30 1	5	6	3 3	4	2

172

30 5	2	3	4 1	24 4	6
18 1	3	6	4	12 2	30 5
12 2	20 1	4 4	90 5	6	3
6	4	2 1	3	5 5	2
12 4	5	2	6	3 3	1
3	60 6	5	2	4 1	4

173

6:1	24:6	30:3	5	2	4:4
2	4	5:5	12:3	90:6	1
3	6:1	6	4	5	12:2
120:4	30:5	2:2	1	3	6
6	3	4:1	40:2	4	5
5	2	4	18:6	1	3

174

120:5	4	6	12:2	4:1	90:3
1:1	6:3	2	6	4	5
24:3	12:2	20:4	1	5	6
2	1	15:3	120:5	6	4
4	6	5	6:3	2	1
30:6	5	1	24:4	3	2

175

48:2	4:4	6:3	30:6	1	5
6	2	1	15:3	5	24:4
4	24:1	6	20:5	3	2
45:5	3	4	1	12:2	6
3	30:5	20:2	4	72:6	1
1	6	5	2	4	3

176

90:5	6	3	24:2	24:4	1
24:1	4	20:2	3	6	60:5
6	2	5	4	12:1	3
3:3	5:5	20:1	6	2	4
24:2	1	4	5	36:3	6
4	3	30:6	1	5	2

177

178

179

180

181

[4] 2	[96] 4	6	1	[45] 5	3
1	2	4	[20] 5	3	[120] 6
[108] 3	6	1	4	[144] 2	5
6	[150] 5	2	3	4	1
[60] 5	1	3	[24] 2	6	4
4	3	5	6	1	2

182

[240] 5	[144] 4	[12] 1	2	6	[30] 3
4	2	6	3	1	5
6	[180] 3	4	5	2	[12] 1
2	[150] 5	3	[12] 1	4	6
[6] 1	6	5	[480] 4	3	2
3	1	2	6	5	4

183

[10] 2	[4608] 1	4	6	[15] 3	5
5	3	[72000] 6	4	1	2
[432] 6	4	3	5	2	[24] 1
3	5	2	1	6	4
4	2	1	[270] 3	5	6
1	6	5	2	4	3

184

[20] 5	1	[576] 4	6	2	[1080] 3
[18] 3	4	6	2	5	1
1	[21600] 5	2	3	4	6
6	2	3	[4] 4	1	[300] 5
[24] 2	6	1	5	3	4
4	3	5	1	6	2

185

³⁶⁰ 5	2	3	1	³⁶⁰ 4	6
4	3	1	²¹⁶ 6	2	5
1	²¹⁶⁰⁰ 4	5	⁷²⁰⁰ 2	6	3
6	1	2	5	3	³² 4
3	5	6	4	1	2
2	6	4	3	5	1

186

⁶ 1	⁶⁰ 5	6	2	⁶⁰ 3	4
6	³⁶⁰ 2	4	3	5	1
⁴⁰ 5	1	3	³²⁴⁰ 6	⁸ 4	2
2	4	5	1	6	3
³⁶ 4	3	¹⁰ 1	5	2	6
3	⁴⁸ 6	2	4	1	5

187

⁶⁰ 1	5	6	⁷² 4	2	3
⁴³²⁰ 4	1	2	3	¹⁸⁰ 6	5
2	3	⁸⁰⁰ 5	1	4	6
3	⁴⁸ 6	4	2	5	1
5	⁶⁰ 4	1	¹⁸ 6	3	2
6	2	3	5	1	4

188

¹⁸⁰ 4	3	¹²⁰⁰ 5	2	²⁴ 1	6
3	5	²⁴ 2	4	6	1
6	2	1	5	²¹⁶⁰⁰ 3	4
¹⁰ 1	²⁵⁹² 6	4	3	5	2
5	4	6	² 1	2	3
2	1	3	6	4	5

189

6480 1	6	3	5	4	180 2
3	40 2	4	1440 1	6	5
5	1	2	4	3	6
192 2	4	6	3	5	144 1
6	75 3	5	2	1	4
4	5	1	6	2	3

190

180 2	6	18 1	3	120 5	4
5	3	6	60 4	180 2	1
61440 4	2	5	1	3	6
18 1	4	3	5	6	30 2
6	5	4	2	1	3
3	1	2	6	4	5

191

7+ 2	5	11+ 4	2- 1	2- 6	2- 3
7+ 1	10+ 6	2	3	4	5
6	4	5	6+ 2	3	1
12+ 3	1- 2	1- 6	5	5+ 1	4
4	3	12+ 1	6	5	2 2
5	8+ 1	3	4	8+ 2	6

192

5- 6	1	4- 2	12+ 4	5	3
3- 1	4	6	5+ 3	2	15+ 5
3- 5	2	3- 4	1	13+ 3	6
9+ 3	8+ 5	3+ 1	2	6	4
2	3	11+ 5	6	4	3+ 1
4	14+ 6	3	5	1 1	2

193

⁹⁺3	⁹⁺4	¹⁻2	1	¹¹⁺5	6
6	5	⁶⁺1	⁶⁺2	4	²⁻3
⁷⁺4	3	5	⁴⁻6	2	1
⁷⁺5	²⁻1	3	¹⁻4	⁴⁻6	2
2	¹⁰⁺6	4	3	¹1	⁹⁺5
¹1	⁸⁺2	6	²⁻5	3	4

194

¹¹⁺6	2	3	⁹⁺5	4	⁴⁻1
¹¹⁺4	1	6	⁴⁻2	⁸⁺3	5
¹⁻2	3	⁸⁺1	6	5	⁴4
⁴⁺3	⁹⁺5	2	⁸⁺4	⁵⁻1	6
1	4	5	3	⁴⁻6	2
¹⁵⁺5	6	4	1	¹⁻2	3

195

⁴⁻1	²2	¹¹⁺4	¹⁰⁺5	3	¹²⁺6
5	¹¹⁺3	1	6	2	4
3	5	¹⁻6	⁹⁺1	4	2
³⁺2	1	5	4	¹⁻6	²⁻3
¹⁶⁺6	²⁻4	2	⁸⁺3	5	1
4	6	3	2	⁴⁻1	5

196

¹⁵⁺4	5	⁹⁺3	1	³⁻6	⁷⁺2
6	²⁻2	4	5	3	1
⁸⁺2	⁵⁺1	¹⁴⁺6	3	5	4
5	3	1	²⁻2	4	¹⁴⁺6
1	¹⁻6	5	²⁻4	¹⁻2	3
⁷⁺3	4	²2	6	1	5

197

¹⁻4	¹⁻1	2	¹⁴⁺3	6	5
5	¹²⁺2	6	4	⁶⁺3	1
⁹⁺1	²⁻4	¹⁻5	6	2	⁹⁺3
2	6	³3	⁸⁺1	¹⁻5	4
6	⁴⁺3	1	5	4	2
¹²⁺3	5	4	2	⁷⁺1	6

198

²⁻3	¹²⁺4	6	2	⁸⁺1	5
5	¹⁻3	4	⁵⁻1	6	2
⁴⁻6	2	⁹⁺1	¹¹⁺5	¹¹⁺3	4
⁷⁺2	⁵5	3	6	4	⁵⁻1
4	⁹⁺1	5	¹⁻3	¹⁰⁺2	6
1	6	2	4	5	3

199

¹⁴⁺2	³⁻3	6	⁴⁻5	1	²¹⁺4
6	1	3	2	4	5
²⁻5	2	⁸⁺4	1	3	6
3	²⁴⁺6	5	4	⁸⁺2	1
³⁻4	5	⁶⁺1	3	¹⁷⁺6	2
1	4	2	6	5	3

200

¹⁻2	3	²⁰⁺5	4	6	³⁻1
⁶6	²⁻1	3	5	¹⁻2	4
²²⁺4	⁸⁺5	2	1	3	¹⁰⁺6
5	6	⁷⁺4	2	1	3
3	4	1	¹¹⁺6	5	²⁰⁺2
¹⁻1	2	6	3	4	5

201

¹⁸⁺4	⁵⁺2	1	¹¹⁺5	6	⁸⁺3
5	3	2	⁵⁻6	1	4
¹¹⁺6	5	²⁴⁺3	1	²⁻4	2
3	1	5	⁶⁺4	2	⁵⁻6
2	6	4	¹⁸⁺3	5	1
³⁻1	4	6	2	3	5

202

⁵⁻1	6	¹³⁺3	2	²⁻4	⁴⁻5
⁷⁺5	3	4	²⁴⁺6	2	1
2	1	6	4	5	3
¹⁻4	5	⁷⁺2	²⁻3	1	¹⁹⁺6
⁹⁺3	4	1	5	6	2
6	⁸⁺2	5	1	⁷⁺3	4

203

²⁸⁺5	3	2	⁵⁻1	6	⁹⁺4
2	6	¹⁻3	4	¹⁶⁺1	5
1	4	¹²⁺5	2	3	⁴⁻6
¹³⁺3	5	1	6	4	2
6	¹⁻1	¹⁻4	5	2	3
4	2	¹⁴⁺6	3	5	1

204

¹¹⁺1	¹⁵⁺3	6	⁴⁷⁺2	¹⁻5	4
3	6	2	5	4	⁴⁻1
6	1	4	3	⁵⁺2	5
¹¹⁺4	5	3	6	1	2
5	2	1	4	6	¹³⁺3
2	¹⁻4	5	1	3	6

205

5 [29+]	6	3	2 [35+]	4	1 [5−]
2 [4+]	1	4	5	3 [8+]	6
1	5 [26+]	6	4	2	3
3	2	5	1	6 [2−]	4
4	3	1	6	5	2 [3−]
6	4	2	3	1	5

206

5 [13+]	2	4 [19+]	6	3	1
6	3 [1−]	2	1 [15+]	4	5
3 [2−]	6 [28+]	1	4	5	2 [11+]
1	4	5	2	6	3
2 [6+]	5	6	3 [8+]	1 [1−]	4 [10+]
4	1 [2−]	3	5	2	6

207

6 [21+]	5	4	2 [1−]	3 [51+]	1
2 [4+]	1	6	3	5	4
1	3 [2−]	5	4	6	2
5 [1−]	6 [4−]	2	1 [10+]	4	3
4	2 [10+]	3	5	1	6
3	4	1	6	2	5

208

5 [23+]	2 [6+]	4	1 [5−]	6	3 [9+]
6	5	3	2 [11+]	1	4
2 [9+]	4	6	3	5 [41+]	1
3	1	2 [1−]	5	4	6
4 [3−]	3	1	6	2 [3−]	5
1	6	5	4	3 [1−]	2

209

8+ 1	2	40+ 5	3− 4	3	15+ 6
3	4− 5	6	1	2	4
2	1	4	5	6	3
10+ 6	4	1− 1	3	5	2
18+ 4	3	2	6	4− 1	5
5	6	10+ 3	2	4	1

210

13+ 1	5	43+ 3	6	12+ 4	2
4	1− 1	5	12+ 2	3	6
3	2	6	2− 1	5	3− 4
3− 5	6	4	3	2	1
2	3	1− 1	20+ 4	6	5
6	4	2	5	2− 1	3

211

2× 1	2	30× 5	12× 4	18× 3	6
2÷ 2	6÷ 1	6	3	4× 4	5 5
4	6	2÷ 2	5 5	1	3÷ 3
15× 3	5	4	12× 2	6	1
30× 5	12× 3	6÷ 1	6	10× 2	2÷ 4
6	4	3÷ 3	1	5	2

212

5 5	15× 3	2÷ 2	2÷ 1	24× 6	4
12× 3	5	4	2	2÷ 1	18× 6
4	6÷ 6	1	15× 5	2	3
4÷ 1	4	30× 6	3	10× 5	2
12× 6	2÷ 2	5	4 4	3÷ 3	1
2	1	2÷ 3	6	20× 4	5

213

36× 6	3	2	60× 5	4÷ 1	60× 4
40× 5	6× 1	6	2	4	3
2	4÷ 4	1	6	30× 3	5
4	90× 6	5	3	2	6÷ 1
6× 3	2	4÷ 4	1	5	6
15× 1	5	3	4 4	3÷ 6	2

214

5÷ 5	1	6÷ 6	3	24× 4	2
18× 3	6 6	1	40× 2	5	4
6	2÷ 2	4	20× 5	3× 3	1
1	10× 5	2	4	12× 6	90× 3
60× 4	3	5	1	2	6
2÷ 2	4	2÷ 3	6	1	5

215

60× 6	2	12× 4	3	20× 1	5
2÷ 2	5	3 3	1	4	2÷ 6
1	16× 4	180× 5	6	30× 2	3
4	1	6	5	3	8× 2
90× 5	3÷ 3	1	60× 2	6	4
3	6	2÷ 2	4	5	1

216

2÷ 1	2	54× 6	3	100× 5	4
3÷ 6	60× 4	3	2÷ 1	2	5
2	3	5	2÷ 4	6× 1	6 6
60× 3	5	4	2	6	1
20× 5	1	12× 2	90× 6	24× 4	3
4	6	1	5	3	2

217

4÷ 1	4	2÷ 3	6	10× 5	2
36× 3	2	100× 4	5	1	24× 6
6	30× 1	5	18× 3	2	4
5	6	36× 2	4· 4	3	1
2÷ 2	3	6	20× 1	4	5
4	5÷ 5	1	36× 2	6	3

218

30× 6	5	60× 2	2÷ 4	12× 3	1
1	6	5	2	4	2÷ 3
30× 3	2	120× 4	5	2÷ 1	6
5	12× 1	6	9× 3	2	40× 4
2÷ 2	4	3	1	180× 6	5
4	3	1· 1	6	5	2

219

24× 1	3	180× 5	2	6	2÷ 4
720× 5	4	6÷ 6	1	3	2
6	2	2÷ 1	360× 5	4	30× 3
4	6	2	3	5	1
90× 3	4÷ 1	4	6	2	120× 5
2	5	3	4	1	6

220

180× 2	6	60× 5	1	4	3
5	3	2÷ 4	2	18× 1	144× 6
120× 4	5	2	6	3	1
2÷ 1	2	3	75× 5	6	4
2÷ 6	4÷ 4	1	3	5	80× 2
3	6÷ 1	6	4	2	5

221

2÷ 2	**5÷** 5	1	**432×** 6	4	3
4	**72×** 1	3	**150×** 5	2	6
4÷ 1	4	6	**2÷** 2	3	**10×** 5
54× 3	6	4	1	5	2
300× 5	3	**2÷** 2	4	**72×** 6	1
6	2	5	3	1	4

222

48× 4	**6÷** 1	6	**60×** 3	5	**2÷** 2
2	6	**180×** 3	5	4	1
1	**120×** 2	5	4	3	**180×** 6
450× 3	4	**2÷** 1	2	6	5
5	3	**2÷** 2	**36×** 6	**4÷** 1	4
6	5	4	1	2	3

223

2÷ 6	**25920×** 4	5	3	1	**2÷** 2
3	**2000×** 5	6	2	4	1
2	1	4	5	6	3
5	**36×** 6	**240×** 2	1	**24×** 3	4
4÷ 4	3	**3÷** 1	6	2	**30×** 5
1	2	3	4	5	6

224

3÷ 3	1	**4800×** 4	2	6	5
48× 6	4	5	**360×** 1	3	**2÷** 2
4	2	**51840×** 6	3	5	1
150× 5	6	**18×** 1	4	2	3
2÷ 2	5	3	6	1	4
1	3	2	5	4	6

225

4320× 2	3÷ 3	1	96× 4	6	120× 5
3	5	6	1	4	2
4	2÷ 1	2	6	10× 5	3
60× 5	24× 6	4	450× 3	2	1
6	2	3	5	1	4
4÷ 1	4	5	2	2÷ 3	6

226

2÷ 2	4	360× 5	3	1	6
12× 1	2÷ 2	12960× 6	4	45× 3	5
4	1	2	5	120× 6	3
3	6	1	12× 2	5	4
150× 5	3	4	6	2÷ 2	1
6	5	3	1	2÷ 4	2

227

12× 2	6	1296× 4	3	5÷ 1	5
20× 1	5	6	1440× 2	3	48× 4
4	1	3	6	5	2
600× 5	3	40× 2	1	4	6
2÷ 6	4	1	5	2	3÷ 3
3	2	5	4	6	1

228

2÷ 4	2	4320× 3	150× 6	5	1
18× 3	6	4	2÷ 2	1	5
6	1	23040× 5	4	2	3
2	5	1	90× 3	6	4
15× 1	3	6	5	4	2
5	2÷ 4	2	3÷ 1	3	6

229

$360\times$ 5	$24\times$ 6	4	$6\times$ 2	3	$40\times$ 1
3	1	$30\times$ 6	5	2	4
6	4	$1440\times$ 2	$2\div$ 3	$4\div$ 1	5
1	3	5	6	4	$3\div$ 2
4	2	3	$5\times$ 1	5	6
2	$20\times$ 5	1	4	$2\div$ 6	3

230

$2\div$ 6	3	$9600\times$ 4	5	$2\div$ 2	1
4	6	5	2	1	$57600\times$ 3
$24\times$ 3	2	$60\times$ 1	4	5	6
2	4	6	$3\div$ 1	$2\div$ 3	5
$5\div$ 1	5	2	3	6	4
5	$18\times$ 1	3	6	4	2

231

$2\div$ 2	$3+$ 1	$24\times$ 6	4	$8+$ 5	3
4	2	$10\times$ 5	$2\div$ 6	3	1
$5-$ 6	$15\times$ 3	2	$1-$ 1	$9+$ 4	5
1	5	$3\div$ 3	2	$24\times$ 6	4
$1-$ 3	4	1	$8+$ 5	$2\div$ 2	$3\div$ 6
5	$2-$ 6	4	3	1	2

232

$5+$ 1	4	5	$2\div$ 3	$8\times$ 2	$3\div$ 6
5	$4+$ 1	3	6	4	2
$4-$ 2	6	$2-$ 4	$5\div$ 5	1	$3\times$ 3
$2-$ 6	$6\times$ 3	2	$1-$ 4	5	1
4	2	$7+$ 6	1	$8+$ 3	5
$2-$ 3	5	$2\div$ 1	2	$10+$ 6	4

233

20× 4	5	7+ 1	6	2÷ 2	3÷ 3
9+ 6	5+ 3	10× 2	5	4	1
3	2	4 4	6÷ 1	6	1− 5
2× 2	1− 4	5	7+ 3	5÷ 1	6
1	5− 6	3− 3	4	5	6+ 2
5 5	1	1− 6	2	3	4

234

9+ 2	6	1	1− 3	15× 5	10+ 4
6 6	20× 4	5	2	3	1
6× 3	2	11+ 4	6	1	5
10+ 1	30× 5	6	2− 4	2	2÷ 3
5	1− 3	2	5÷ 1	4 4	6
4	4+ 1	3	5	3÷ 6	2

235

3÷ 1	11+ 4	2	5	12× 6	10+ 3
3	5− 6	4÷ 4	1	2	5
10× 5	1	2÷ 6	3	8+ 4	2
2	3 3	4− 5	4	12+ 1	2− 6
30× 6	5	1	2	3	4
9+ 4	2	3	6	6+ 5	1

236

4× 4	13+ 2	6	1 1	2− 5	3
1	5	2÷ 2	4	3× 3	1− 6
3÷ 2	6	13+ 4	3	1	5
10+ 3	4	5÷ 5	6	2× 2	1
1− 5	3	1	11+ 2	12+ 6	4
6	3× 1	3	5	4	2

237

3 (8+)	4 (1−)	5	1 (4×)	6 (12×)	2
2	3	1 (1)	4	5 (4−)	6 (10+)
6 (12×)	2	4 (1−)	5	1	3
4 (10+)	5	3 (2÷)	6	2 (9+)	1
1	6 (12×)	2	3	4	5 (12+)
5 (5÷)	1	6 (3÷)	2	3	4

238

4 (10+)	6 (6)	1 (8+)	5 (2−)	3	2 (3÷)
5	1	4	3	2 (1−)	6
2 (2÷)	3 (2−)	5	6 (3÷)	1	4 (12+)
1	4 (9+)	3	2	6 (24×)	5
6 (30×)	5	2	1 (4×)	4	3
3 (11+)	2	6	4	5 (4−)	1

239

3 (11+)	6 (3÷)	5 (5×)	1 (7+)	4	2
6	2	1	3 (15×)	5	4 (1−)
2	3 (8+)	4 (11+)	6	1	5
1 (5÷)	5	6 (13+)	4 (2÷)	2	3 (2−)
5	4	3	2 (10×)	6 (15+)	1
4 (3−)	1	2 (2)	5	3	6

240

3 (1−)	2	1 (10+)	6 (3÷)	4 (20×)	5
4 (2−)	3	6	2	5 (15×)	1 (1−)
6	5 (5)	4 (4×)	1	3	2
1 (8+)	4	3	5 (10+)	2 (2÷)	6 (13+)
5 (13+)	6	2	3	1	4
2	1 (5÷)	5	4 (2−)	6	3

241

120× 6	4	5	9+ 3	1	1− 2
150× 2	5	4	1	18+ 6	3
5	2÷ 1	2− 3	4	2	6
3	2	1	288× 6	4	5÷ 5
4÷ 4	11+ 3	6	2	300× 5	1
1	6	2	5	3	4

242

480× 6	4	1− 2	3	90× 1	5
4	5÷ 5	1	24× 6	3	2÷ 2
5	9+ 2	3	1	6	4
1	3	600× 5	4	9+ 2	6
3− 3	6	4	120× 2	5	1
2÷ 2	1	6	5	4	3

243

3÷ 3	1	2− 5	14+ 6	2	4
2÷ 1	13+ 6	3	2	360× 4	5
2	4	1	60× 3	5	6
60× 5	2	4	1	6÷ 6	3
4	3	144× 6	5 5	1	1− 2
30× 6	5	2	4	3	1

244

32× 4	10+ 3	6	1	120× 2	5
1	3− 5	2	4	3	10+ 6
2	4	300× 3	5	120× 6	1
14+ 5	6	4	3÷ 2	1	3
2÷ 3	1	5	6	4	2− 2
6	2	3÷ 1	3	5	4

245

²2	¹⁰⁺6	¹⁻4	3	¹⁰⁰ˣ5	¹⁻1
3	1	³⁰ˣ5	6	4	2
⁷²ˣ4	3	2	5	1	¹⁹⁺6
¹⁵⁰ˣ6	5	3	²÷1	2	4
5	²÷2	⁴÷1	4	6	3
1	4	¹⁸⁰ˣ6	2	3	5

246

¹⁻3	4	³⁶⁰⁰ˣ5	2	¹⁰⁺1	6
³⁻1	5	2	6	3	²÷4
4	¹⁸ˣ3	6	⁵ˣ1	⁶⁰⁰ˣ5	2
³÷2	6	1	5	4	3
6	1	¹⁻3	4	2	5
¹¹⁺5	2	4	²÷3	6	1

247

⁴⁸ˣ4	²÷6	3	⁵÷1	5	¹⁸⁰ˣ2
6	³²⁰⁰ˣ4	2	5	3	1
2	⁶ˣ3	5	4	1	6
1	2	4	³⁻3	6	5
²⁰⁺3	5	1	6	²²⁺2	4
5	1	6	2	4	3

248

⁵÷5	1	⁶⁰⁰ˣ3	4	³⁶ˣ2	6
¹⁰⁺6	²÷2	4	5	3	¹⁻1
3	³⁰ˣ6	5	1	⁹⁶ˣ4	2
1	5	2	¹⁻3	6	4
²÷4	²¹⁶⁰ˣ3	6	2	⁹⁺1	5
2	4	1	6	5	3

312

249

^{1−}4	^{120×}1	2	6	^{15×}5	3
3	^{2÷}4	^{2−}6	2	1	5
^{150×}5	2	4	^{4÷}1	^{36×}3	¹¹⁺6
6	5	¹⁵⁺3	4	2	1
^{2÷}2	3	1	5	6	4
1	^{30×}6	5	3	^{2÷}4	2

250

^{5÷}5	1	^{360×}3	¹⁵⁺4	6	⁸⁺2
¹⁷⁺4	3	2	1	5	6
3	2	6	5	^{4÷}4	1
1	6	^{3−}4	^{54×}3	^{3−}2	5
^{3÷}2	^{1−}5	1	6	3	^{120×}4
6	4	5	2	1	3

251

⁸4	¹⁶7	2	¹⁷5	6	3	⁴1
3	1	7	⁴6	4	2	¹³5
⁶5	¹⁴3	⁷4	1	2	6	¹²7
1	5	6	¹⁴7	3	4	2
¹⁶6	4	⁶1	¹⁰2	5	¹⁵7	3
¹¹2	6	5	3	7	1	¹⁵4
7	2	³3	⁵4	1	5	6

252

⁴4	¹⁸6	¹²3	⁶2	¹³1	5	7
7	5	2	1	3	¹⁶4	6
⁴2	1	7	¹⁰3	5	6	⁸4
1	⁹4	¹⁷5	6	2	⁹7	3
¹⁴5	3	6	¹⁵7	4	2	1
6	2	¹²1	4	¹⁸7	⁸3	5
3	7	4	5	6	³1	2

253

3	7	2	5	6	1	4
5	3	6	4	2	7	1
7	5	1	2	4	3	6
4	2	3	6	1	5	7
2	6	7	1	5	4	3
6	1	4	3	7	2	5
1	4	5	7	3	6	2

254

6	3	4	5	2	7	1
7	4	1	3	5	6	2
1	5	2	6	4	3	7
3	7	5	2	1	4	6
2	1	7	4	6	5	3
5	6	3	1	7	2	4
4	2	6	7	3	1	5

255

2	1	6	4	3	5	7
7	2	5	3	1	4	6
5	7	4	6	2	1	3
6	4	7	2	5	3	1
3	5	2	1	6	7	4
1	6	3	7	4	2	5
4	3	1	5	7	6	2

256

2	7	6	3	5	4	1
7	6	5	4	2	1	3
1	5	7	2	4	3	6
6	1	4	5	3	2	7
4	3	2	1	6	7	5
5	4	3	7	1	6	2
3	2	1	6	7	5	4

257

¹⁰1	2	7	¹²4	¹⁰3	¹³5	6
¹⁵3	7	⁵5	6	1	2	¹⁴4
5	1	⁸4	2	6	7	3
⁶4	3	¹¹1	¹⁴7	2	⁹6	¹²5
2	4	6	¹⁰1	5	3	7
¹³7	6	⁸3	5	4	⁴1	2
¹¹6	5	2	3	¹¹7	4	1

258

¹⁵5	¹⁴6	⁶1	4	¹²7	3	2
7	2	6	1	¹⁷4	¹²5	3
3	¹⁶5	⁹2	7	6	4	⁸1
⁶4	7	5	2	⁴3	1	6
2	4	⁹3	6	1	¹⁹7	5
⁸1	3	4	¹³5	2	6	7
¹⁴6	1	7	³3	¹¹5	2	4

259

¹²4	¹²7	3	2	¹¹1	5	¹³6
7	⁹1	4	³3	5	¹¹6	2
1	4	¹⁸7	6	2	3	5
⁸3	2	5	¹³4	¹⁴6	7	1
¹⁷6	3	⁴1	5	4	2	¹⁴7
5	6	2	1	¹⁷7	4	3
¹³2	5	6	7	3	1	4

260

⁶4	2	¹⁵5	¹¹3	7	⁷1	⁶6
⁷7	⁹3	6	1	4	2	¹⁸5
1	5	4	⁷2	3	6	7
¹⁴6	¹⁰4	⁸1	¹²7	2	¹¹5	3
5	6	7	4	1	3	³2
3	¹⁰7	¹⁰2	¹⁵6	5	4	1
2	1	3	5	¹⁷6	7	4

261

4	2	7	1	5	3	6
3	6	1	5	4	7	2
7	4	5	6	2	1	3
6	3	2	7	1	4	5
1	5	6	3	7	2	4
2	1	3	4	6	5	7
5	7	4	2	3	6	1

262

3	5	6	2	7	1	4
5	3	1	7	4	2	6
7	2	5	6	3	4	1
2	1	7	4	5	6	3
6	4	2	3	1	5	7
1	7	4	5	6	3	2
4	6	3	1	2	7	5

263

1	3	7	6	4	2	5
5	7	1	4	3	6	2
7	4	6	2	5	3	1
6	2	5	3	7	1	4
2	5	4	1	6	7	3
3	6	2	5	1	4	7
4	1	3	7	2	5	6

264

6	7	2	3	1	4	5
4	1	6	2	5	3	7
7	3	1	4	6	5	2
5	2	3	7	4	6	1
2	6	7	5	3	1	4
1	5	4	6	7	2	3
3	4	5	1	2	7	6

265

13		15			5	
2	6	3	5	7	1	4
5	3	7	4	6	2	1
1	2	5	7	3	4	6
4	5	1	3	2	6	7
3	1	4	6	5	7	2
6	7	2	1	4	5	3
7	4	6	2	1	3	5

Cage clues: 13, 15, 5, 6, 12, 13, 12, 22, 13, 26, 4, 20, 23, 12

266

17	24				15	
2	4	3	6	5	7	1
4	5	1	2	6	3	7
6	2	7	1	3	5	4
1	3	5	4	7	2	6
5	1	2	7	4	6	3
7	6	4	3	2	1	5
3	7	6	5	1	4	2

Cage clues: 17, 24, 15, 7, 8, 14, 24, 7, 15, 9, 28, 11, 11, 6

267

32	7			16		22
7	2	4	1	3	5	6
6	5	7	3	1	4	2
2	7	3	5	6	1	4
1	6	2	4	5	3	7
4	1	5	6	7	2	3
3	4	1	7	2	6	5
5	3	6	2	4	7	1

Cage clues: 32, 7, 16, 22, 7, 8, 12, 22, 5, 20, 8, 12, 17, 8

268

14	10		9			19
6	1	7	2	3	4	5
4	2	3	1	5	7	6
3	7	2	5	6	1	4
1	4	5	7	2	6	3
5	6	4	3	1	2	7
7	5	1	6	4	3	2
2	3	6	4	7	5	1

Cage clues: 14, 10, 9, 19, 18, 26, 26, 20, 12, 17, 17, 3, 5

269

ⁱ³7	¹⁴5	4	²¹1	¹⁵6	⁵3	2
6	3	2	5	1	4	¹³7
¹⁶3	2	5	7	⁴4	1	6
4	²⁰7	6	3	²³5	2	1
2	¹¹1	7	4	3	6	5
5	4	⁶1	¹⁵6	2	¹⁹7	3
¹1	6	3	2	7	5	4

270

¹³4	1	²¹2	7	²⁰3	5	6
5	¹⁹7	4	2	6	⁴1	3
3	5	7	6	¹²2	4	1
¹³6	2	1	4	¹⁰7	3	5
¹³1	⁶6	²³3	5	⁸4	¹³7	¹⁵2
2	4	5	3	1	6	7
7	3	6	⁶1	5	2	4

271

²⁶6	1	3	4	¹⁹5	7	⁷2
4	¹⁷6	5	1	7	2	3
³1	4	2	²¹3	6	5	7
2	7	¹⁵6	5	⁷4	⁹3	⁶1
¹²7	3	4	2	1	6	5
¹⁴5	2	²⁰7	6	⁴3	1	¹⁶4
3	5	1	7	2	4	6

272

³⁰6	3	5	7	4	³1	⁹2
⁴3	³⁴6	4	1	5	2	7
1	5	²2	6	7	²⁴3	4
4	1	7	2	3	5	¹²6
¹²5	7	⁶3	⁹4	2	¹⁶6	1
¹³7	2	1	3	6	4	5
2	4	¹¹6	5	¹¹1	7	3

318

273

2	6	4	5	1	3	7
4	7	3	6	2	1	5
5	2	1	4	7	6	3
3	5	2	1	4	7	6
1	3	5	7	6	4	2
6	4	7	3	5	2	1
7	1	6	2	3	5	4

274

5	3	7	1	2	6	4
3	7	2	4	6	5	1
2	6	3	7	1	4	5
1	4	5	6	7	2	3
4	2	6	5	3	1	7
7	5	1	2	4	3	6
6	1	4	3	5	7	2

275

1	4	5	6	3	2	7
7	2	3	4	5	1	6
2	1	6	5	7	4	3
4	3	2	7	6	5	1
3	7	4	1	2	6	5
5	6	1	3	4	7	2
6	5	7	2	1	3	4

276

1	2	5	3	7	6	4
5	7	1	2	4	3	6
7	4	3	6	5	2	1
3	5	4	7	6	1	2
2	1	6	4	3	5	7
6	3	7	1	2	4	5
4	6	2	5	1	7	3

277

6	1	3	2	7	5	4
2	3	7	4	5	1	6
5	6	4	1	2	7	3
4	2	1	7	6	3	5
1	4	6	5	3	2	7
7	5	2	3	4	6	1
3	7	5	6	1	4	2

278

5	1	4	3	6	7	2
1	6	5	2	7	3	4
2	5	6	7	1	4	3
7	2	3	1	4	5	6
4	3	7	5	2	6	1
6	7	1	4	3	2	5
3	4	2	6	5	1	7

279

2	4	5	1	7	6	3
7	5	1	6	2	3	4
5	3	6	7	4	1	2
3	2	4	5	1	7	6
4	1	2	3	6	5	7
6	7	3	2	5	4	1
1	6	7	4	3	2	5

280

6	3	2	7	4	1	5
2	1	6	5	7	4	3
4	6	5	1	2	3	7
3	4	7	2	6	5	1
7	5	4	3	1	6	2
5	2	1	4	3	7	6
1	7	3	6	5	2	4

281

34	15			21	4	
7	4	6	2	5	3	1
4	7	2	1	3	5	6
6	5	3 (39)	7 (7)	2	1 (5)	4
5	3	7	4	1	6	2
1 (9)	6	5 (14)	3	4	2	7
3	2	1	6 (24)	7 (19)	4	5
2	1 (5)	4	5	6	7	3

282

38		8	8		13	22
7	4	3	2	6	1	5
5	2	4	1	7	3	6
1	3 (14)	6	5	2	7	4
6	1	7 (24)	3	4	5 (9)	2 (3)
2 (2)	7	5 (8)	6	3 (4)	4	1
3 (13)	5	2	4	1	6 (13)	7
4	6	1	7 (17)	5	2	3

283

14		32		5	9	
6	1	3	7	2	4	5
1 (29)	7	4	5 (22)	3	6	2 (3)
4	5	7	3	6	2	1
2	6	5	4 (22)	1 (17)	7 (27)	3
3	4	2	6	5	1 (4)	7
5	2	6	1 (7)	7	3	4
7	3	1	2	4	5 (5)	6

284

8	10	13			7	
6	2	7	5	1	4	3
2	4	1	3	6 (11)	5 (12)	7
3 (4)	1	6 (22)	2	5	7 (9)	4 (14)
5 (19)	7	4	6 (43)	3	2	1
7	3 (3)	5	4	2	1	6
4 (10)	5	3 (11)	1	7	6	2
1	6	2	7	4	3	5

285

²⁹7	¹⁰3	1	4	2	³⁵5	6
4	⁷1	²⁵7	6	5	2	3
6	4	2	7	3	1	5
5	7	⁶4	2	⁴²6	3	1
¹⁸3	6	5	1	7	4	2
1	2	⁹3	5	4	6	7
⁷2	5	6	⁴3	1	7	⁴4

286

¹⁰3	1	2	⁴³7	5	¹⁰6	4
¹³7	2	1	6	3	4	5
¹⁵5	4	3	³³2	7	⁷1	6
6	¹⁵3	7	5	4	²⁶2	⁴1
4	6	5	1	2	7	3
³2	5	6	4	1	3	7
1	¹¹7	4	3	⁶6	5	2

287

²⁰7	¹⁸3	4	5	1	2	⁴³6
6	7	1	3	4	5	2
⁸1	5	2	²³4	⁹6	3	7
³⁶4	2	6	1	¹⁰3	7	5
3	6	5	2	7	1	4
5	⁷1	7	6	2	4	3
2	4	²²3	7	5	6	1

288

¹⁰4	6	⁷2	1	3	¹⁷7	5
¹⁸2	3	7	6	1	5	¹⁶4
⁶6	¹³5	¹⁴1	¹⁴4	7	3	2
1	7	3	¹⁵5	⁹2	4	6
⁴⁶5	2	4	7	6	1	¹¹3
7	4	6	3	5	2	1
3	1	5	2	4	6	7

289

5	6	4	7	3	2	1
2	7	3	4	5	1	6
3	2	5	1	6	4	7
1	4	2	6	7	5	3
4	5	6	3	1	7	2
7	3	1	2	4	6	5
6	1	7	5	2	3	4

290

5	1	6	3	7	4	2
6	2	4	7	3	5	1
1	4	5	6	2	7	3
2	3	1	5	4	6	7
3	6	7	4	1	2	5
4	7	2	1	5	3	6
7	5	3	2	6	1	4

291

1	3	7	4	2	6	5
2	7	5	3	6	1	4
7	5	4	6	1	3	2
5	2	6	1	3	4	7
6	4	1	5	7	2	3
3	6	2	7	4	5	1
4	1	3	2	5	7	6

292

5	1	2	4	7	3	6
1	6	5	3	4	2	7
7	3	1	2	6	5	4
6	7	3	5	1	4	2
4	5	7	6	2	1	3
2	4	6	1	3	7	5
3	2	4	7	5	6	1

293

7	6	2	4	1	3	5
5	1	4	3	7	6	2
1	3	6	2	5	4	7
3	4	5	7	6	2	1
6	2	1	5	3	7	4
2	7	3	1	4	5	6
4	5	7	6	2	1	3

294

5	3	2	7	1	4	6
2	6	5	3	7	1	4
4	1	7	5	2	6	3
6	2	3	4	5	7	1
7	4	1	6	3	5	2
3	5	6	1	4	2	7
1	7	4	2	6	3	5

295

6	5	2	3	7	4	1
7	1	3	5	4	2	6
4	3	6	1	2	5	7
5	2	1	4	6	7	3
2	7	4	6	1	3	5
1	4	5	7	3	6	2
3	6	7	2	5	1	4

296

3	7	2	1	5	6	4
6	4	7	3	2	5	1
5	2	6	4	1	3	7
1	5	4	2	3	7	6
4	6	1	5	7	2	3
2	1	3	7	6	4	5
7	3	5	6	4	1	2

297

84			18		40	
4	3	7	6	1	2	5
1	6	5	3	2	4	7
3	4	1	5	6	7	2
6	2	4	7	5	1	3
5	7	6	2	4	3	1
7	5	2	1	3	6	4
2	1	3	4	7	5	6

(cage clues: 84, 18, 40, 24, 20, 84, 42, 36, 70, 5, 3, 70, 84, 72, 4, 15, 4, 210)

298

70		21	18		8	
2	5	7	6	3	4	1
7	4	3	1	5	6	2
3	6	5	4	2	1	7
5	1	6	7	4	2	3
4	2	1	3	7	5	6
6	3	2	5	1	7	4
1	7	4	2	6	3	5

(cage clues: 70, 21, 18, 8, 24, 60, 60, 30, 112, 2, 21, 36, 105, 120, 8, 12, 7, 15)

299

70			120		9	
2	7	5	6	4	1	3
7	4	6	2	5	3	1
4	5	7	3	1	2	6
3	6	1	7	2	5	4
6	3	2	1	7	4	5
5	1	3	4	6	7	2
1	2	4	5	3	6	7

(cage clues: 70, 120, 9, 140, 84, 24, 12, 21, 20, 6, 36, 42, 56, 5, 10, 12, 20, 126)

300

4	84		35			36
4	2	6	5	7	1	3
1	5	7	3	6	4	2
2	4	1	7	5	3	6
7	3	2	1	4	6	5
5	6	3	4	1	2	7
6	1	5	2	3	7	4
3	7	4	6	2	5	1

(cage clues: 4, 84, 35, 36, 14, 60, 90, 72, 7, 24, 8, 140, 90, 42, 120, 12, 35)

301

180 1	5	6	392 7	2	4	75 3
6	392 2	36 3	12 4	1	7	5
4	7	2	6	3	5	1
7	32 4	15 1	3	240 5	2	252 6
2	1	4	5	6	3	7
90 5	210 3	7	1	4	168 6	2
3	6	5	2	7	1	4

302

72 1	3	315 5	112 4	7	2	240 6
6	20 1	3	7	2	5	4
4	5	84 7	3	90 6	1	2
14 7	4	2	6	1	3	5
2	12 6	20 1	5	4	252 7	3
105 5	2	48 6	1	3	4	210 7
3	7	4	2	5	6	1

303

140 2	400 5	4	18 1	3	6	84 7
7	2	5	4	252 6	1	3
5	6 6	1	3	2	7	4
24 4	1	504 6	56 2	7	30 3	5
6	7	3	150 5	1	4	2
3 3	4	294 7	6	5	240 2	1
1	3	2	7	4	5	6

304

56 2	4	20 1	5	378 6	7	3
1	7	70 5	4	3	420 2	24 6
360 3	6	7	2	4 1	5	4
5	252 2	3	1	4	6	7
4	30 1	6	7	150 2	3	5
42 7	3	72 4	6	5	2 1	2
6	5	2	3	28 7	4	1

326

305

²⁵²6	2	3	⁴²7	⁹⁰5	1	³⁶⁰4
7	⁷⁰1	2	3	⁸⁰4	6	5
2	7	4	5	1	3	6
5	¹²⁰4	6	¹⁶1	2	²⁴⁵7	3
⁷²3	6	1	4	7	5	⁵⁶2
1	¹⁰⁵3	5	2	²¹⁶6	4	7
4	5	7	6	3	2	1

306

⁴²3	2	²⁴⁰6	¹⁴⁰7	5	4	⁹⁰1
⁸1	7	5	2	4	⁸⁴6	3
2	4	³⁵1	5	⁹3	7	6
¹²⁰4	6	7	3	1	2	5
²¹⁰7	1	⁷²3	¹⁴⁴4	6	²¹⁰5	2
6	5	2	1	7	3	⁵⁶4
5	3	4	6	2	1	7

307

¹⁵⁰3	⁸⁴6	7	¹²⁶1	¹⁴⁴2	¹⁴⁰5	4
5	1	2	3	6	4	7
2	5	⁹⁶4	6	7	3	1
6	4	1	⁴²7	¹⁰5	2	⁹⁰3
¹⁹⁶4	7	3	2	1	6	5
7	³⁰2	5	¹²⁰4	³3	1	³³⁶6
1	3	6	5	4	7	2

308

⁵5	1	²¹⁶3	4	6	⁵⁶2	7
¹⁴1	³⁰6	5	3	¹⁴⁰7	4	¹⁸⁰2
7	2	1	5	4	3	6
¹¹²4	7	¹²6	1	2	5	⁶⁰3
¹⁸⁰3	4	²⁸7	2	⁹⁰1	6	5
6	5	2	⁵⁰⁴7	3	1	4
2	3	4	6	5	⁷7	1

327

309

1 ⁵	3 ⁵⁰⁴	4	6	2 ¹²	7 ¹⁴⁰	5
5	7	2	3	1	4	6 ¹²
6 ⁷²	4	7 ⁴²⁰	2	5	3 ³¹⁵	1
3	1	6	4 ⁴	7	5	2
7 ²⁸⁰	2 ¹⁸⁰	5	1	3	6 ¹⁶⁸	4
2	6	3	5 ²¹⁰	4 ²⁴	1	7
4	5	1	7	6	2	3

310

3 ³⁶	2 ⁸⁴	1	6	7 ²¹⁰	5	4 ¹²
6	5 ²¹⁰	2	7	4 ³⁰⁰	1	3
2	4 ⁹⁶	7	3	5	6	1
4	6	3	5	1 ⁸	2	7 ³⁵
1 ³⁵	7 ²⁵²	6	2	3 ⁷²	4	5
5	3	4	1	6	7 ⁸⁴	2
7	1	5 ¹²⁰	4	2	3	6

311

2 ³⁶	3	6	7 ¹⁶⁸⁰⁰	1	4	5
1 ⁹⁰	6 ¹²	7 ⁴²	2	3	5	4 ¹¹⁷⁶
5	2	1 ¹⁴⁴	3	4	6	7
3	1 ³¹³⁶⁰	5	4	6	7	2
6	7	4	5 ³⁰	2	3	1 ³
7	4	2	6	5 ⁴²⁰	1	3
4	5 ¹⁵	3	1	7	2	6

312

3 ²¹	7	6 ⁴²	1	5 ³⁰	2 ³²	4
5 ⁵⁰⁴⁰	1	7	3	2	4	6 ⁵⁰⁴
4	3	5 ¹⁰⁸⁰	2	7	6	1
6	2	1	4	3	7 ²⁹⁴⁰⁰	5 ⁷⁰
7	4 ²⁴	3	6	1	5	2
1	6	2 ⁸⁰	5	4	3 ⁹	7
2	5	4	7	6	1	3

313

30 6	5	84 1	24 4	3	56 7	2
28 1	7	6	60 5	2	15 3	4
4	144 3	2	1	6	5	84 7
7	6	17640 3	2	20 5	4	1
15 3	4	5	7	1	2	6
5	2	7	6	4	90 1	3
8 2	1	4	21 3	7	6	5

314

8 2	4	2520 6	21 7	3	120 5	1
120 4	7	5	6	1	2	3 3
6	5	4 1	2	42 7	3	4
70 5	1	4	360 3	6	28 7	2520 2
7	2	3	1	5	4	6
36 3	6	2	140 5	4	1	7
3 1	3	7	4	2	6	5

315

30 6	24 3	4	280 1	2	5	7
5	840 1	2	21 3	7	36 6	4
7	6	5	6720 4	1	2	3
1	7	6	5	90 3	24 4	2
4	2	42 1	7	6	3	30 5
30 2	4	3	6	5	28 7	1
3	5	7	2	4	1	6

316

4 1	4	6720 6	7	68040 3	2	30 5
2	1	4	5	7	3	6
4	28 2	7	3	5	6	1
105 5	3	2	1	6	84 7	4
7	3150 5	1	192 6	56 2	4	3
18 3	6	5	2	4	1	7
6	7	3	4	10 1	5	2

317

⁵⁷⁶4	2	⁴⁴¹⁰3	1	7	5	6
6	²⁵²⁰⁰4	5	2	3	²¹1	7
2	6	1	5	²⁰4	7	3
¹⁰⁵⁰1	7	6	⁷²4	5	³⁶3	2
7	5	2	3	1	6	⁸⁰4
3	⁸⁴1	7	6	⁸⁴2	4	5
5	3	4	7	6	²2	1

318

⁸⁴2	²⁴4	6	¹⁴⁰7	5	3	⁶1
7	6	1	4	¹⁰⁵3	5	2
⁷²⁰⁰4	⁵⁷⁶2	3	6	1	7	³⁵5
6	3	4	5	2	1	7
5	³⁵1	²¹⁰7	2	4	³⁶6	3
³1	7	5	3	⁴²6	2	⁹⁶4
3	5	2	1	7	4	6

319

⁶6	⁸⁸²⁰⁰3	7	5	4	¹²1	2
⁶1	³⁰2	5	¹⁶⁸4	7	6	⁷⁰⁵⁶3
2	5	3	7	6	4	1
3	²⁰1	⁵⁷⁶2	6	⁹⁰⁰5	7	4
5	4	6	2	1	3	7
¹⁹⁶7	6	4	1	3	2	³⁰5
4	7	1	3	2	5	6

320

⁷⁰7	5	¹⁶⁸6	⁴⁰4	2	1	²⁵²3
2	7	4	5	⁶1	³3	6
⁵⁰⁴3	¹²⁰4	5	1	6	7	2
1	6	⁶⁷²⁰2	7	3	¹²⁰5	4
4	2	7	3	5	6	³⁵1
³⁰5	⁹3	1	⁸⁴6	4	2	7
6	1	3	2	7	4	5

321

³⁰²⁴4	³⁰5	1	6	⁴²7	2	3
1	6	³⁰5	3	⁶⁰4	⁵⁶7	2
3	7	6	2	5	4	⁴²1
³⁰5	1	¹²2	²⁰¹⁶⁰4	3	6	7
6	2	3	7	1	5	4
⁵⁶2	4	³⁵7	1	6	3	³⁰5
7	¹²3	4	5	2	1	6

322

³⁰1	5	6	³⁶3	¹⁶⁸4	7	¹⁰2
²⁵²⁰⁰5	2	7	4	3	6	1
⁶3	6	⁹⁴⁰⁸4	7	2	⁵1	5
2	4	3	1	6	5	⁸⁴7
⁶6	1	5	¹⁰2	7	3	4
¹⁹⁶7	³⁶⁰3	2	5	1	4	¹⁸6
4	7	1	6	5	2	3

323

⁸⁴6	2	²⁰4	1	5	¹⁴¹¹²3	⁵⁶7
7	³⁰5	1	³⁰3	6	4	2
³⁰3	6	2	5	7	³⁷⁸⁰1	4
2	³1	3	7	4	6	5
5	²⁴4	6	⁴2	1	7	3
²⁸1	⁷⁵⁶⁰3	7	4	2	¹⁰5	6
4	7	5	6	3	2	1

324

⁴⁰2	5	²⁶⁴⁶6	1	7	²⁴3	4
³⁰6	4	3	7	²⁰5	2	¹²1
5	²¹7	1	3	4	6	2
1	3	²⁰4	¹²⁶⁰2	6	5	7
⁷⁰⁵⁶4	1	5	6	²⁴⁰2	⁵⁶7	3
3	2	7	5	³1	4	³⁰6
7	6	2	4	3	1	5

325

20			36288			
1	5	4	7	2	3	6
35				6		
5	7	6	2	1	4	3
37800			72		40	
3	1	7	4	6	2	5
				105		
6	2	1	3	7	5	4
24					84	7
2	4	5	6	3	7	1
168			20			
4	3	2	1	5	6	7
7	6	3	5	4	1	2

326

79380					40	
5	7	1	6	3	2	4
	4800			4		
2	6	3	7	4	1	5
				294		36
3	5	2	4	6	7	1
12						
1	2	4	5	7	6	3
	630		20			
6	3	7	1	5	4	2
112			6		30	42
7	4	5	2	1	3	6
4	1	6	3	2	5	7

327

8064			30			6
7	6	4	5	2	3	1
		60	210		28	
3	4	6	7	5	1	2
				9072		
4	5	2	6	1	7	3
60		3				700
5	2	3	1	6	4	7
	42					
6	3	1	2	7	5	4
70						
2	1	7	4	3	6	5
1	7	5	3	4	2	6

328

21			4200			12
3	7	1	2	4	5	6
24		5040				
6	4	2	3	5	7	1
42				120		
7	1	6	5	3	4	2
20						
4	6	3	7	2	1	5
	105			6	36	84
1	3	5	4	6	2	7
	20		168			
5	2	7	6	1	3	4
2	5	4	1	7	6	3

329

20·1	4	21·7	3	2520·6	5	2
5	24·2	4	12·1	3	6	7
14·7	3	840·1	5	4	12·2	6
2	1	30·6	4	7	3	20·5
72·3	17640·6	5	7	2	1	4
4	5	2	6	1	7	3·3
6	42·7	3	2	20·5	4	1

330

900·3	6	2	5	112·7	4	1
1	28·7	36·3	6	10·2	5	4
5	4	1	2	2520·6	3	8820·7
60·4	3	42·6	7	5	1	2
168·6	5	7	1	4	12·2	3
7	2	720·4	3	1	6	5
2	1	5	4	3	7	6

331

5+·1	2	3−·3	4	9+·5	10+·7	6
2	15+·5	6	3	4	1	7
17+·7	6	4	2	6+·1	10+·5	3
6	4	7·7	1	13+·3	2	15+·5
1−·5	2−·3	1	7	2	6	4
4	5−·7	2	5	19+·6	2−·3	1
9+·3	1	5	6	7	2−·4	2

332

17·4	6	15+·3	5	7	4+·1	2
1−·6	7	8+·4	3	1−·5	11+·2	1
7	9+·2	5	1	4	3	6
10+·3	1−·5	2	11+·7	1	2−·6	4
2	4	5−·1	6	3	15+·5	4−·7
5	5+·1	17+·7	2·2	6	4	3
1	3	6	4	14+·2	7	5

333

¹⁴⁺1	6	⁵⁻2	7	²⁻5	⁹⁺3	4
7	¹⁵⁺4	6	⁴⁺1	3	2	¹⁵⁺5
²⁻2	5	¹⁶⁺7	3	¹1	4	6
4	⁶⁻1	3	6	³⁻7	¹³⁺5	2
²⁻5	7	³⁺1	2	4	6	¹¹⁺3
3	¹¹⁺2	4	5	¹⁻6	7	1
¹⁴⁺6	3	5	⁷⁺4	2	1	7

334

⁶⁺3	2	1	¹⁴⁺5	¹⁻4	¹⁹⁺7	6
¹⁻1	⁷7	5	4	3	6	²⁻2
2	⁴⁻3	7	⁵⁻1	6	¹⁴⁺5	4
¹⁶⁺6	5	⁸⁺4	3	1	2	7
5	¹²⁺1	¹¹⁺6	¹³⁺2	7	4	⁹⁺3
7	4	2	¹⁸⁺6	5	⁶⁺3	1
²⁻4	6	3	7	2	1	5

335

¹³⁺6	4	3	¹⁹⁺5	7	⁸⁺2	1
¹⁵⁺3	⁴⁻2	⁹⁺1	7	¹²⁺4	6	5
7	6	5	3	2	¹⁰⁺1	⁴4
5	²⁻3	¹¹⁺6	4	1	7	2
⁷⁺1	5	⁵⁻7	2	¹⁻3	4	³⁻6
2	¹²⁺7	4	1	¹⁷⁺6	¹⁵⁺5	3
4	¹⁻1	2	6	5	3	7

336

¹⁻3	¹⁴⁺1	6	7	¹³⁺4	2	²⁻5
2	¹³⁺6	¹⁰⁺4	1	5	7	3
⁷7	5	⁵⁻2	⁸⁺4	3	⁵⁻6	1
¹⁶⁺5	2	7	²⁻3	1	⁷⁺4	⁶6
4	7	⁷⁺3	5	¹⁵⁺6	1	2
¹¹⁺6	3	1	¹³⁺2	7	¹⁻5	4
1	4	5	6	2	⁴⁻3	7

337

3 (12+)	5	4 (3−)	7 (5−)	2	1 (10+)	6
6 (1−)	4	7	1 (12+)	5 (7+)	2	3
5	3 (6+)	1	6	4 (3−)	7	2 (12+)
7 (6−)	1	2	5	3 (3)	6	4
4 (17+)	6	3 (14+)	2 (2−)	7 (2−)	5	1 (13+)
2 (5+)	7	6	4	1 (4+)	3	5
1	2	5	3 (13+)	6	4	7

338

4 (3−)	5 (1−)	3 (4+)	1	7 (15+)	2	6
7	4	6 (4−)	2	1 (9+)	5	3
3 (12+)	7	2	6 (1−)	5	1 (11+)	4
1 (5+)	2	5 (14+)	4	3 (10+)	6	7 (6−)
2	6 (1−)	7	5	4	3	1
5 (14+)	3	1 (6+)	7 (15+)	6	4 (2−)	2
6	1	4	3 (3)	2	7	5 (2−)

339

3 (4−)	7	5 (5)	2 (4−)	6	4 (10+)	1
7 (15+)	4 (7+)	3 (14+)	6	2 (1−)	1	5
6	1	2	5 (14+)	7	3 (1−)	4
2	5 (4−)	1	4	3	7 (13+)	6
5 (11+)	2	4	7 (11+)	1 (4−)	6 (11+)	3
4 (8+)	3	6 (19+)	1	5	2	7 (5−)
1	6	7	3	4 (1−)	5	2

340

7 (12+)	2	3	1 (4−)	5	6 (2−)	4
1 (5−)	7 (13+)	6 (17+)	3 (1−)	2	4 (12+)	5
6	5	4	2 (10+)	1	7	3
5 (2−)	1	7	4 (11+)	3	2 (8+)	6
3	6 (9+)	2	5 (12+)	4	1 (10+)	7
4 (2−)	3 (12+)	1	7	6 (19+)	5 (5)	2
2	4	5	6	7	3 (2−)	1

341

²⁻6	²²⁺5	4	7	⁷⁺3	2	⁶⁻1
4	6	⁶⁺1	5	2	¹³⁺3	7
⁶⁺1	⁵⁻7	2	¹²⁺3	5	4	6
3	2	²¹⁺7	4	⁵⁻1	6	¹⁵⁺5
¹⁴⁺2	3	5	¹⁻1	²⁰⁺6	7	4
5	⁵⁺4	6	2	7	1	3
7	1	⁹⁺3	6	¹⁻4	5	2

342

¹⁻4	³⁺1	²⁻5	3	⁵⁻6	¹²⁺7	2
5	2	²⁵⁺4	7	1	3	²⁸⁺6
¹¹⁺1	7	3	4	¹²⁺2	6	5
7	3	⁴⁻2	6	5	1	4
¹⁻6	5	⁴⁺1	2	3	⁴⁻4	7
⁹⁺2	4	¹⁹⁺6	1	7	¹⁶⁺5	⁴⁺3
3	6	7	5	4	2	1

343

¹⁶⁺6	3	2	4	¹²⁺7	⁸⁺1	5
¹³⁺3	²⁰⁺6	7	1	5	¹⁹⁺4	2
1	7	¹⁵⁺4	5	3	2	⁵⁻6
4	¹¹⁺5	6	3	¹⁻2	7	1
5	¹⁻4	3	⁴⁻2	1	6	⁷7
¹²⁺7	2	1	6	²⁵⁺4	5	¹⁻3
2	⁴⁻1	5	7	6	3	4

344

²2	²²⁺6	7	¹⁴⁺5	4	1	3
²⁰⁺7	3	4	2	²⁰⁺5	¹⁵⁺6	1
6	7	¹³⁺1	3	2	4	5
¹⁴⁺5	2	6	1	7	3	²⁻4
4	1	3	¹⁸⁺7	6	5	2
3	⁹⁺4	³⁻5	⁵⁻6	1	⁵⁻2	7
1	5	2	¹⁻4	3	¹³⁺7	6

345

3 (12+)	5	1	6 (10+)	7 (20+)	2 (2-)	4
1	2	5 (21+)	4	6	7	3 (4-)
5 (25+)	4	3	2 (7+)	1 (5-)	6	7
6	7	4	3	2	5 (4-)	1 (17+)
7	3	2	5 (1-)	4	1	6
4 (6+)	6 (7+)	7 (6-)	1	5 (25+)	3	2
2	1	6	7	3	4	5

346

3 (2-)	2 (17+)	4	6 (13+)	7	1	5 (4-)
1	4	7	5 (18+)	3 (1-)	6 (25+)	2
5 (22+)	3	1	4	2	7	6
2	6	5	7 (13+)	1 (10+)	3	4
4	5	3	1	6 (11+)	2	7 (6-)
6 (20+)	7	2	3 (17+)	5	4	1
7	1 (5-)	6	2	4	5	3

347

2 (2-)	4	1 (6-)	7	5 (22+)	3 (3-)	6
1 (12+)	3	5 (2-)	4	6	7	2 (6+)
6 (28+)	2	3	1 (1)	7 (2-)	5	4
3	6	4 (9+)	5	1 (13+)	2	7
5	7	2 (4-)	6	4 (15+)	1	3
7	1 (7+)	6	3 (8+)	2	4	5 (6+)
4 (1-)	5	7 (5-)	2	3	6	1

348

2 (3-)	5	6 (13+)	1 (12+)	7	3 (1-)	4
6 (3-)	2	1	4	3 (26+)	5	7
3	7 (20+)	4	6	5	2 (3+)	1
5 (16+)	6	7	3 (2-)	1	4 (16+)	2 (16+)
7	3 (1-)	2	5	4	1	6
4	1 (11+)	5 (12+)	7	2	6 (19+)	3
1	4	3	2	6	7	5

349

[2−]1	3	[7]7	[22+]6	5	[2−]4	2
[15+]2	5	3	[2−]4	7	[5−]6	1
[6−]7	1	5	2	4	[13+]3	[27+]6
[17+]5	6	[3−]4	1	3	2	7
6	[6−]7	1	3	2	5	4
[13+]3	4	[14+]2	[13+]7	6	[11+]1	5
4	2	6	5	1	7	3

350

[6+]3	1	2	[17+]6	[16+]5	7	4
[2−]5	3	7	4	[2−]2	[4−]6	[2−]1
[5−]6	[6−]7	1	[25+]5	4	2	3
1	6	4	3	7	[25+]5	2
[13+]2	5	[2−]3	1	[11+]6	4	7
4	2	[13+]6	7	1	[2−]3	5
[21+]7	4	5	2	3	1	6

351

[1−]4	5	[4+]1	2	[14+]3	[20+]7	6
[10+]6	[18+]4	7	1	5	3	[14+]2
1	7	[9+]2	3	6	4	5
3	[6+]1	4	[4−]6	2	[1−]5	7
[43+]5	2	3	[6−]7	1	6	[7+]4
7	3	6	5	[3−]4	2	1
2	6	5	4	7	[2−]1	3

352

[14+]6	[4+]3	1	[31+]2	5	4	[6−]7
2	6	[1−]7	[18+]5	[3−]4	3	1
[11+]5	4	6	1	7	2	[14+]3
[18+]7	2	4	6	[7+]3	1	5
4	7	2	3	1	5	6
[4−]1	5	[15+]3	[2−]4	6	7	2
[4+]3	1	5	7	[12+]2	6	4

353

7 (12+)	4 (5+)	3 (2-)	1	2 (18+)	5	6
5	1	7 (31+)	6	4	3	2
2	3	4	5	6 (5-)	1 (6-)	7
3 (1-)	6 (16+)	5	2 (33+)	1	7 (20+)	4 (10+)
4	5	2	3	7	6	1
1	7	6	4	3 (8+)	2 (9+)	5
6 (4-)	2	1	7	5	4	3

354

2 (18+)	1 (6-)	7 (12+)	5	3 (3-)	6	4 (3-)
4	7	5 (14+)	3	6	2 (13+)	1
5	2	3	7 (6-)	1	4	6
6 (1-)	5	2	1	4 (14+)	3	7 (23+)
1 (8+)	3	4	6 (22+)	7	5	2
7 (4-)	4	6	2	5 (14+)	1	3
3	6 (5-)	1	4	2	7	5

355

1 (1-)	4 (16+)	3 (41+)	7	2	6 (1-)	5
2	5	7	3	4	1 (23+)	6
3 (13+)	6	2 (5+)	4	7	5	1 (30+)
4	2	1	5	6	7	3
7 (17+)	3	5	6 (1-)	1	4 (5-)	2
5 (1-)	7	6	1 (7+)	3	2	4
6	1 (1+)	4	2	5	3	7

356

6 (18+)	2 (14+)	4	3 (14+)	1 (6-)	7	5 (12+)
5	3	1	6	4 (6+)	2	7
7	4	6 (18+)	5	2 (16+)	3	1
2 (2-)	5	7	1 (10+)	3	6	4
4	1 (30+)	2	7	6	5 (1-)	3 (3-)
1	7	3	2 (14+)	5	4	6
3	6	5 (1-)	4	7	1 (3+)	2

357

6 ^(10+)	5 ^(13+)	7	1	4 ^(15+)	3 ^(1−)	2
3	2 ^(6+)	1	6	5	4 ^(17+)	7
1	3	2 ^(1−)	5 ^(12+)	7	6	4 ^(43+)
4 ^(3−)	1	3	7 ^(16+)	2 ^(1−)	5	6
7 ^(20+)	6	5	4	3	2	1
5 ^(11+)	7	4 ^(2−)	2	6 ^(5−)	1	3
2	4	6	3	1	7	5

358

5 ^(16+)	4	7	2 ^(28+)	3 ^(4+)	1	6
1 ^(34+)	2	5	6	4	7	3
7	3	6	4	1	5	2 ^(2)
3 ^(15+)	5 ^(15+)	2 ^(3+)	1	7 ^(1−)	6	4 ^(3−)
2	1	4	5	6 ^(1−)	3 ^(15+)	7
4	6 ^(1−)	3 ^(4−)	7	5	2	1
6	7	1 ^(6+)	3	2	4	5

359

2 ^(2−)	1 ^(17+)	4 ^(11+)	7	6 ^(15+)	3	5 ^(4−)
4	3	7 ^(6−)	2 ^(10+)	5 ^(49+)	6	1
7	6	1	5	4	2	3
5 ^(13+)	2	6	3	1 ^(4+)	7	4
3 ^(10+)	7 ^(12+)	5	1	2	4	6
1	4 ^(9+)	3 ^(1−)	6 ^(2−)	7	5	2
6	5	2	4	3 ^(11+)	1	7

360

4 ^(12+)	5 ^(11+)	6 ^(21+)	7 ^(6−)	3 ^(1−)	2	1 ^(24+)
2	6	4	1	7 ^(12+)	5	3
6	4	7	2 ^(1−)	1	3	5
3 ^(2−)	7 ^(27+)	1 ^(10+)	6	5 ^(17+)	4	2
1	2	5	3	4	7 ^(20+)	6
5	1	3 ^(1−)	4	2	6	7
7	3 ^(10+)	2	5	6	1 ^(3−)	4

361

³⁻5	2	³⁴⁺6	⁴⁺3	⁸⁺4	⁶⁻7	1
²¹⁺4	7	5	1	3	6	2
7	3	2	4	1	⁵5	¹⁸⁺6
1	6	4	¹⁹⁺2	5	3	7
2	4	¹⁵⁺3	7	6	1	5
³⁻6	¹⁴⁺1	7	5	2	²⁻4	¹⁻3
3	5	1	¹⁻6	7	2	4

362

¹¹⁺1	7	⁵⁺3	2	¹⁵⁺5	¹⁰⁺6	4
¹⁵⁺6	3	1	5	4	⁶⁻7	¹⁻2
4	²⁸⁺5	6	7	⁸⁺2	1	3
5	6	²⁻7	4	3	2	1
¹²⁺7	²2	5	³⁻3	²¹⁺1	4	¹⁻6
2	⁵⁺1	4	6	7	3	5
3	⁷⁺4	2	1	6	²⁻5	7

363

²⁻3	¹⁹⁺7	5	⁹⁺1	6	¹⁰⁺4	2
1	²³⁺5	7	¹³⁺6	2	⁹⁺3	4
7	2	6	3	4	1	5
¹⁵⁺5	⁴4	3	¹⁻2	1	²⁰ᵢ7	6
4	6	⁴⁻1	5	⁴¹⁺3	2	7
¹⁻2	3	4	7	5	¹¹⁺6	²⁻1
6	1	2	4	7	5	3

364

¹⁵⁺3	5	7	⁴⁺1	2	²⁻6	4
³³⁺4	2	6	3	1	7	5
¹⁻5	³⁻6	¹¹⁺4	2	3	1	⁶7
6	3	2	5	³⁻7	4	1
¹⁰⁺7	1	¹⁻5	6	¹⁵⁺4	3	2
2	¹²⁺7	⁵⁺1	4	6	¹⁴⁺5	3
1	4	⁴⁻3	7	⁷⁺5	2	6

365

³⁴⁺3	⁶6	2	1	7	5	⁴³⁺4
6	1	4	5	¹⁻3	2	7
³⁻2	5	⁶⁻1	7	6	4	3
¹⁻1	2	¹²⁺5	3	⁷⁺4	7	6
¹²⁺5	²³⁺7	3	4	2	6	⁹⁺1
7	¹¹⁺4	6	¹³⁺2	1	3	5
4	3	7	6	5	¹⁻1	2

366

¹¹⁺2	6	3	¹⁷⁺7	¹⁰⁺1	5	4
¹⁴⁺5	³⁻4	1	3	7	¹⁻2	⁹⁺6
4	5	¹⁷⁺7	6	¹⁴⁺2	3	1
²⁻1	3	⁶6	4	5	7	2
¹³⁺7	2	4	¹⁻1	³⁶⁺3	6	⁸⁺5
³⁻6	⁸⁺7	³⁻5	2	4	1	3
3	1	2	5	6	4	7

367

¹¹⁺5	¹⁻4	¹⁸⁺1	³⁶⁺6	7	¹⁻2	3
4	3	5	7	6	¹⁰⁺1	2
2	²⁻1	3	5	4	¹⁴⁺6	7
¹³⁺6	7	²⁷⁺2	4	1	3	5
3	2	7	1	5	4	¹¹⁺6
⁴⁻1	5	6	2	3	¹²⁺7	4
⁷7	¹⁰⁺6	4	¹⁻3	2	5	1

368

³¹⁺5	7	4	¹⁰⁺1	6	¹⁰⁺3	2
7	³⁻4	1	3	¹⁻2	¹⁰⁺6	5
6	2	¹⁹⁺7	5	3	4	²⁻1
²⁻1	¹⁶⁺6	5	7	⁷⁺4	2	3
3	5	²⁻2	4	1	⁴²⁺7	6
⁷⁺2	1	¹²⁺3	6	7	5	4
4	3	6	⁸⁺2	5	1	7

369

21+ 2	1	5	7	11+ 3	4	14+ 6
5	42+ 7	1	6 6	4	1- 2	3
4	2	6	4- 3	7	1	5
6- 1	3	1- 2	7+ 4	4- 5	31+ 6	7
7	6	3	2	1	5	7+ 4
3	5	15+ 4	1	6	7	2
6	4	7	10+ 5	2	3	1

370

1- 5	6	21+ 2	8+ 3	1	20+ 7	12+ 4
2- 1	3	5	4	7	6	2
3	4	7	1- 2	30+ 5	1	6
4- 6	2	1- 3	1	6+ 4	5	6- 7
16+ 7	5	4	17+ 6	2	3	1
4	6- 7	1	5	6	2	2- 3
1- 2	1	6 6	7	3	4	5

371

6× 3	210× 5	6	7	30× 2	4÷ 1	4
2	1	112× 7	4	5	3	84× 6
36× 1	6	4	30× 5	3	7	2
6	7 7	45× 3	2	4÷ 1	4	5÷ 5
140× 4	3	5	84× 6	7	2	1
7	2÷ 4	2÷ 2	1	120× 6	5	126× 3
5	2	3÷ 1	3	4	6	7

372

4× 4	1	150× 5	6	42× 3	7	2
1	36× 3	4	5	245× 7	36× 2	6÷ 6
2÷ 2	4	3	7	5	6	1
210× 5	7	6	2÷ 2	2÷ 1	3	140× 4
90× 3	6	2÷ 1	4	2	5	7
84× 7	5	2	6÷ 1	6	20× 4	3 3
6	2	84× 7	3	4	1	5

373

84× 7	4	3	20× 5	2	42× 1	2÷ 6
5÷ 5	1	4 4	2	7	6	3
42× 1	6	7	120× 4	5	30× 3	2
18× 2	3	2÷ 1	6	168× 4	7	5
3	210× 5	2	21× 7	6	4÷ 4	1
6	7	30× 5	3	1	2÷ 2	4
2÷ 4	2	6	1	105× 3	5	7

374

2÷ 1	2	210× 5	6	42× 3	7	80× 4
18× 3	1	6	7	2	4	5
56× 4	90× 5	2÷ 1	2	105× 7	2÷ 6	3
2	6	16× 4	1	5	3	7÷ 7
7	3	42× 2	4	60× 6	5	1
120× 5	4	7	3	4÷ 1	2	6 6
6	105× 7	3	5	4	2÷ 1	2

375

2÷ 6	3	60× 5	3÷ 1	196× 4	7	2÷ 2
35× 5	2	6	3	7	40× 4	1
1	140× 4	7	48× 6	3÷ 3	2	5
7	5	4	2	1	108× 6	3
28× 4	7	1	140× 5	30× 2	3	6
36× 2	6	3	4	5	7÷ 1	7
3 3	2÷ 1	2	7	120× 6	5	4

376

90× 5	6	30× 3	48× 2	4÷ 1	4	35× 7
3	56× 7	2	6	4	1	5
2	4	5	6÷ 1	6	42× 7	3
1 1	140× 5	7	4	2÷ 3	6	2
48× 4	2÷ 3	6	175× 5	7	6× 2	1
6	2	7÷ 1	7	5	3	120× 4
7÷ 7	1	24× 4	3	2	5	6

377

4 (80×)	2 (12×)	6	1 (3÷)	3	7 (70×)	5
5	4	1	6 (6)	7 (84×)	2	3 (3÷)
2 (70×)	7	5	3	4	6 (36×)	1
1 (3÷)	5 (140×)	4	7	2	3	6 (120×)
3	6 (2÷)	7 (42×)	2 (2÷)	1	5	4
6 (42×)	3	2	4 (100×)	5	1 (7÷)	7
7	1	3	5	6 (48×)	4	2

378

4 (2÷)	6 (60×)	2	5 (35×)	7 (126×)	3	1 (4÷)
2	5	7	1	3 (42×)	6	4
1 (5÷)	4 (72×)	6	3	2	7	5 (70×)
5	1 (1)	3 (84×)	4 (48×)	6	2	7
6 (126×)	3	4	7	1 (5÷)	5	2
7	2 (42×)	1 (5÷)	6 (60×)	5	4 (16×)	3 (2÷)
3	7	5	2	4	1	6

379

5 (210×)	7	2 (2÷)	4	6 (2÷)	3	1 (28×)
6	2 (24×)	1 (30×)	5 (60×)	3	7 (7÷)	4
2	6	5	3 (3:)	4	1	7
7 (63×)	3	6	1	2 (2÷)	4	5 (30×)
3	5 (20×)	4	7 (42×)	1	6	2
4 (4÷)	1	7 (84×)	6 (6)	5 (70×)	2 (60×)	3
1	4	3	2	7	5	6

380

3 (126×)	6 (60×)	5	1 (6×)	2	4 (140×)	7
7	2	1 (4÷)	4	3	5	6 (72×)
6	5 (105×)	3	7 (?÷)	1	2	4
2 (2÷)	4	7 (84×)	6 (30×)	5	1	3
1 (20×)	3	4	5 (140×)	7	6 (36×)	2
5	7 (7÷)	6 (24×)	2	4	3	1 (5÷)
4	1	2 (2÷)	3	6	7	5

381

180×			360×	2÷		7÷
6	3	5	4	2	1	7
2	168× 7	6	5	1	420× 3	4
28× 1	2	4	3	5	7	180× 6
4	5÷ 1	3	14× 7	720× 6	5	2
7	5	1	2	504× 4	6	3
420× 3	3÷ 6	2	1	7	4	5
5	4	7	6	3	2÷ 2	1

382

2÷ 4	2	5÷ 1	5	36× 6	420× 7	3
252× 7	6	2	1	3	4	5
1	420× 4	5	3	336× 2	6	7
6	3÷ 1	3	7	280× 5	2	4
180× 2	5	6	4	7	3÷ 3	6× 1
105× 5	3	168× 7	2÷ 2	4	1	6
3	7	4	6	10× 1	5	2

383

1050× 6	5	7	2÷ 4	2	3÷ 1	3
5	120× 2	3	2÷ 1	1008× 6	4	7
3÷ 3	1	5	2	245× 7	6	120× 4
168× 1	6	4	7	5	3	2
168× 2	4	60× 6	2÷ 3	35× 1	7	5
4	7	2	6	144× 3	5	1
7	3	1	5	4	2	6

384

2÷ 6	3÷ 2	3÷ 1	3	980× 7	4	10× 5
3	6	336× 4	2	5	7	1
70× 5	7	6	80× 4	3÷ 1	3	2
2	1	7	5	4	2÷ 6	3
180× 4	3	180× 5	1	6	56× 2	7
7× 7	5	3	60× 6	2	1	4
1	168× 4	2	7	3	5	6

346

385

^{4÷}1	4	^{20×}5	^{504×}6	7	2	^{105×}3
^{504×}3	7	1	4	^{12×}2	6	5
^{100×}5	6	4	2	3	^{3÷}1	7
4	5	^{294×}7	1	6	3	^{2÷}2
^{72×}2	^{2÷}3	6	7	^{140×}4	5	1
6	2	3	^{150×}5	1	7	^{96×}4
^{7÷}7	1	2	3	5	4	6

386

^{288×}4	6	^{210×}5	2	7	^{105×}3	1
6	^{2÷}2	4	3	^{6÷}1	5	7
2	^{504×}3	^{7÷}1	7	6	^{360×}4	^{120×}5
^{245×}1	4	7	5	3	6	2
5	7	6	^{24×}1	4	^{2÷}2	3
7	^{120×}5	3	6	^{420×}2	1	4
^{3÷}3	1	2	4	5	7	6

387

^{120×}2	^{2÷}3	6	^{56×}1	4	7	^{5÷}5
3	4	5	^{315×}7	2	^{288×}6	1
^{24×}6	1	^{490×}7	3	5	4	2
4	7	2	5	3	^{2÷}1	6
^{210×}5	6	^{4÷}1	4	^{126×}7	2	^{420×}3
7	^{180×}2	3	6	1	5	4
1	5	^{2÷}4	2	6	3	7

388

^{252×}3	^{40×}5	2	1	^{54×}6	^{840×}4	7
6	2	7	4	1	3	5
^{84×}1	7	4	^{630×}5	3	^{120×}2	6
^{2÷}2	3	^{5÷}1	6	^{420×}7	5	4
4	^{28×}1	5	7	2	6	3
7	4	^{540×}6	3	5	^{2÷}1	2
5	6	3	^{2÷}2	4	^{7÷}7	1

389

³⁄168× 3	4	2	¹²× 6	⁶÷ 1	⁹⁸⁰× 5	7
¹²⁶⁰× 5	³÷ 3	7	2	6	4	²÷ 1
6	1	⁶⁰× 4	3	5	7	2
7	6	1	²÷ 4	2	⁶³⁰× 3	5
²÷ 4	2	²¹⁰× 5	1	7	6	¹⁴⁴× 3
²÷ 1	⁵²⁵× 5	6	7	¹²× 3	2	4
2	7	3	5	4	1	6

390

⁴⁵× 3	1	⁸⁴× 7	2	¹²⁰× 6	5	²÷ 4
5	3	6	1	4	²¹⁰× 7	2
³÷ 2	⁴²⁰× 7	4	3	1	6	5
6	²÷ 4	2	5	²¹⁰× 7	1	³⁷⁸× 3
⁵⁶× 4	2	⁹⁰× 1	6	5	3	7
1	5	3	⁴²⁰× 7	²÷ 2	4	6
7	6	5	4	3	²÷ 2	1

391

³⁵²⁸× 1	²¹¹⁶⁸× 4	3	7	6	³⁰× 5	2
4	¹⁰× 5	6	³³⁶⁰⁰× 1	7	2	3
3	2	7	5	1	6	4
7	6	1	² 2	¹⁸⁰× 3	4	5
⁷⁰× 5	1	¹²× 2	6	4	3	7
2	7	⁶⁰× 4	3	5	⁷÷ 1	⁶÷ 6
²÷ 6	3	5	²÷ 4	2	7	1

392

⁵÷ 5	1	²¹⁰× 6	²³⁵²× 4	3	7	2
⁷²× 6	3	5	2	7	²÷ 1	³⁶⁰× 4
4	¹²× 6	7	⁹⁰× 3	5	2	1
⁸⁴⁰× 7	2	⁸⁴× 4	6	1	5	3
1	4	3	7	⁴⁸× 2	6	¹⁴⁰× 5
3	5	²÷ 2	1	6	4	7
2	³⁵× 7	1	5	4	²÷ 3	6

393

²⁵²ˣ6	²⁴ˣ3	4	²÷1	2	³⁷⁸⁰⁰ˣ7	5
7	6	2	5	3	4	1
²⁰ˣ1	4	6	3	³⁵²⁸⁰ˣ5	²⁵²ˣ2	7
5	²÷2	1	7	4	3	6
²÷2	²¹ˣ1	3	6	7	²⁰ˣ5	4
4	7	¹⁰⁵⁰ˣ5	2	6	1	³⁶ˣ3
3	5	7	⁴÷4	1	6	2

394

³⁰²⁴⁰ˣ4	⁵ˣ5	1	⁶6	¹⁰⁵ˣ7	3	³÷2
7	3	⁵⁶ˣ2	4	⁴²ˣ1	5	6
5	6	4	7	3	2	⁴⁵⁰ˣ1
3	¹⁰⁰⁸ˣ1	¹⁶⁸⁰ˣ6	2	4	7	5
²÷2	4	7	5	6	1	3
1	7	5	³÷3	²⁴⁰ˣ2	6	4
6	2	3	1	5	²⁸ˣ4	7

395

¹⁶⁸ˣ7	2	²÷6	3	²⁰ˣ5	4	1
3	4	⁸⁴⁰ˣ1	6	7	2	5
1	¹⁵ˣ5	3	2	⁷⁰⁵⁶ˣ6	7	4
³⁰ˣ5	6	²÷4	7	2	1	3
²÷4	³÷3	2	⁵ˣ5	1	²⁵²ˣ6	7
2	1	²⁸ˣ7	4	⁶⁰ˣ3	5	6
²¹⁰ˣ6	7	5	1	4	3	⁶ˣ2

396

¹⁵ˣ5	3	²÷6	²⁴⁰ˣ4	²¹⁰ˣ7	²÷1	2
1	¹⁴⁰ˣ7	3	2	5	6	⁸⁴ˣ4
³²²⁵⁶ˣ6	5	4	1	⁴²ˣ3	2	7
2	4	³⁰ˣ1	5	6	7	3
²¹ˣ7	2	5	6	4	³÷3	1
3	6	2	7	1	¹²⁰ˣ4	5
²⁸ˣ4	1	7	³⁰ˣ3	2	5	6

397

15× 3	1	23040× 2	5	2268× 7	6	168× 4
14× 2	5	4	6	3	7	1
7	2	1	3	40× 4	5÷ 5	6
4	3	6	2	5	1	504× 7
180× 5	4	7÷ 7	1	6	3	2
6	35× 7	5	4÷ 4	1	2	60× 3
1	6	42× 3	7	2	4	5

398

42× 6	2÷ 2	1	560× 5	4	7	30× 3
7	1	756× 3	5040× 2	6	4	5
600× 5	3	7	4	1	6	2
4	6	84× 2	3	7	5÷ 5	1
1	5	6	7	2	144× 3	4
42× 3	7	1440× 4	1	5	2	6
2	4	5	6	3	7÷ 1	7

399

2÷ 3	6	2400× 4	5	1	70× 2	7
4	1	3	1008× 7	48× 2	6	5
42× 7	2	5	1	6	4	52920× 3
6	105× 5	7	2	3÷ 3	1	4
1	3	480× 2	4	7	5	6
2	4	6	3	20× 5	7	2÷ 1
5	42× 7	1	6	4	3	2

400

12600× 3	5	7÷ 1	3÷ 2	6	140× 7	4
2 2	4	7	2592× 3	1	5	6
6	7	5	60× 1	4	3	2
14× 7	2	5184× 4	5	3	6	84× 1
20× 1	6	3	4	980× 5	2	7
5	3÷ 1	6	7	2	4	3
4	3	2	6	7	5× 1	5

401

1 (6÷)	6	3 (3150×)	2	4 (40×)	5	7 (42×)
4 (1260×)	3	7	5	2	1	6
7	2 (2)	6 (30×)	3	5	4 (168×)	1 (72×)
3	4 (140×)	5	1	6	7	2
5	7	4 (4÷)	6 (3528×)	1	2	3
2 (3÷)	5	1	7	3	6	4 (60×)
6	1 (2÷)	2	4	7	3	5

402

6 (6÷)	2 (42×)	7	1 (3÷)	3	4 (80×)	5
1	3	5 (5)	7 (70560×)	2	6	4
4 (80640×)	7 (42×)	6	2 (10×)	1	5	3
7	4	1	5	6 (2÷)	3	2
3	5	2	6	4	7	1
5 (5÷)	1	4	3 (36×)	7 (588×)	2	6
2 (3÷)	6	3	4	5 (5×)	1	7

403

4 (28×)	3 (30240×)	6 (30×)	5 (35×)	1	7	2 (8400×)
7	6	5	4 (2÷)	2	3 (3÷)	1
5	2	7	3 (84×)	4	1	6
6	1	3 (6×)	2	7	5	4
3 (42×)	4	1 (4÷)	6 (60×)	5	2	7
2	7	4	1 (1260×)	3	6 (72×)	5
1	5	2	7	6	4	3

404

2 (840×)	6	1	5	7	3 (2÷)	4 (20×)
4 (4)	1	7 (3528×)	3	2	6	5
5 (30×)	3	2	6	4	7	1
6 (60×)	5	4 (3360×)	2	3 (420×)	1	7
7 (21×)	2	3	4	1	5	6 (2÷)
1	4	5	7 (42×)	6 (3÷)	2	3
3	7	6	1	5 (40×)	4	2

405

2÷ 4	1260× 5	3	7	1	2	6
2	105× 3	7	2520× 6	5	1	4
3÷ 6	2	5	20× 1	4	7	3
12× 1	6	2	5	9072× 3	4	350× 7
140× 5	12× 1	4	3	7	6	2
7	4	12× 1	2	6	3	5
21× 3	7	6	2÷ 4	2	5	1

406

42× 7	1	30× 2	3	3600× 5	4	6
24× 4	6	5	2÷ 2	1	7÷ 7	3
6	23520× 7	3	5	4	1	2
3÷ 3	2	30× 1	4	84× 7	6	5
1	5	6	7	6× 3	2	4÷ 4
40× 5	4	3024× 7	6	2	105× 3	1
2	3	4	1	6	5	7

407

6300× 7	5	3	96× 4	12× 6	2	1680× 1
5	84× 3	2	6	4	1	7
4	7	6	525× 1	5	3	2
3÷ 3	3÷ 2	5	7	1	2520× 4	6
1	6	10080× 7	6× 2	3	5	4
6	4	1	3	14× 2	7	5
2÷ 2	1	4	5	7	6	3

408

84× 7	6	41160× 2	1800× 5	1	4	3
2	7	4	3	6	20× 1	5
12× 4	3	2÷ 6	7	5	2	1
720× 6	4	3	350× 1	7	5	2
1	5	7	2	48× 4	18× 3	6
3	1	5	6	2	196× 7	4
5	2	4÷ 1	4	2÷ 3	6	7

409

6 ²÷	7 ¹⁴⁰ˣ	2 ¹²⁶⁰ˣ	5 ⁶⁰ˣ	4 ⁸⁴ˣ	3	1 ⁵÷
3	4	1	6	2	7	5
4 ¹⁴⁴ˣ	5	6	7	3 ⁴²ˣ	1	2
2	3	5	1	7	4 ¹³⁴⁴⁰ˣ	6
1 ¹⁹⁶⁰ˣ	6	3	4	5	2	7
7	1	4	2	6 ¹⁸⁰ˣ	5	3 ¹²ˣ
5	2	7	3 ³÷	1	6	4

410

3 ²⁸⁸ˣ	4	5 ²⁰ˣ	2	6 ³⁰ˣ	7 ⁷÷	1
4	6	2	1	5	3 ⁶³ˣ	7
7 ²⁵²⁰ˣ	1	4	5 ⁹⁶⁰ˣ	2	6	3
5	3	6	7 ⁵²⁹²⁰ˣ	4	1 ²÷	2
2 ²÷	7	3	6	1	4	5 ⁵⁰⁴⁰ˣ
1	5	7	4	3	2	6
6	2	1 ³÷	3	7 ¹⁴⁰ˣ	5	4

411

5 ²⁻	7	1 ⁴÷	4	3 ¹⁶⁺	6	2 ⁶⁰ˣ
3 ¹¹⁺	2 ⁵⁶ˣ	4	1 ³ˣ	7	5	6
2	6	7	3	1	4 ¹⁻	5
1 ¹³⁺	5	3 ¹⁶⁺	7	6	2 ⁴²ˣ	4 ¹²ˣ
7	4 ¹⁶ˣ	5 ¹⁻	6 ¹³⁺	2	3	1
4	1	6	2 ²⁰ˣ	5	7	3
6 ²÷	3	2	5	4 ⁴	1 ⁷÷	7

412

1 ⁷÷	7	6 ³⁰ˣ	5	3 ¹³⁺	2 ²÷	4
5 ¹⁸⁺	6	7	1	4	3 ¹⁻	2
2 ⁴⁻	3 ⁹ˣ	1	4 ²⁻	6	7 ²⁴⁵ˣ	5
6	4 ¹³⁺	3	2	5 ¹⁰ˣ	1 ¹	7
4	5	2 ⁴²ˣ	7	1	6 ²÷	3
7 ¹²⁺	1 ²⁰ˣ	4	3	2	5 ³⁰ˣ	6
3	2	5	6 ¹⁷⁺	7	4	1

413

2−	2÷	3	35×		70×	12+
6	2	3	7	1	5	4
4	1	12× 6	5	7	2	3
4− 7	3	2	1	120× 6	4	5
12+ 1	196× 7	4	13+ 3	5	12× 6	2
5	6	7	4	1− 2	3÷ 3	1
11+ 2	4	5	6	3	1	294× 7
15× 3	5	1	2÷ 2	4	7	6

414

13+	2÷		84×		150×	
7	1	2	3	4	5	6
2	60× 4	3	7	36× 6	7÷ 1	5
4	6 6	5	2	3	7	11+ 1
13+ 1	7	96× 4	6	3− 5	4− 2	3
5	11+ 3	1	4	2	6	7
2÷ 6	60× 2	7	5× 5	1	1− 3	4
3	5	6	1	13+ 7	4	2

415

140×		3−		6÷	12×	
7	4	5	2	6	1	3
2÷ 2	5	11+ 3	14+ 6	1	4	294× 7
4	2÷ 2	1	3	5	7	6
10+ 6	1	7	84× 4	30× 2	3	8+ 5
1	2− 6	4	7	3	5	2
3	42× 7	2	30× 5	2− 4	6	1
5 5	3	6	1	13+ 7	2	4

416

30×		21×			28×	1−
5	2	3	7	1	4	6
3	12+ 4	6	2	7	1	5
9+ 6	1	2	1− 4	5	14+ 3	7
14+ 1	84× 3	7	3÷ 6	2	30× 5	4
7	6	4	15× 5	3	2	2÷ 1
2÷ 4	175× 5	1	3	2− 6	126× 7	2
2	7	5	1 1	4	6	3

354

417

⁹⁺4	1	7	6	³⁰ˣ2	5	¹⁻3
¹⁴⁺1	4	¹¹⁺6	5	⁵⁶ˣ7	3	2
6	7	²÷1	⁶³ˣ3	4	2	³⁰ˣ5
¹⁵ˣ5	³⁶ˣ6	2	7	3	³⁻4	1
3	2	¹¹⁺4	⁵÷1	5	7	6
¹⁴ˣ7	3	5	2	³⁶ˣ6	⁴÷1	4
2	⁶⁰ˣ5	3	4	1	6	⁷7

418

¹³⁺4	3	⁵ˣ1	²÷6	¹⁴⁰ˣ7	5	²2
6	1	5	3	4	⁷⁰ˣ2	7
⁴²ˣ3	2	¹¹²ˣ7	4	⁴⁻6	¹⁰⁺1	5
7	¹⁴⁺5	4	⁵÷1	2	3	6
⁸⁺2	6	3	5	¹²⁺1	7	¹⁻4
1	⁸⁴ˣ7	6	2	²⁻5	4	3
5	⁵⁶ˣ4	2	7	3	⁶÷6	1

419

¹¹⁺6	4	⁵÷1	5	⁴²ˣ3	7	2
1	¹⁻3	4	⁷7	⁹⁺6	2	¹⁻5
⁶⁰ˣ5	6	¹³⁺2	²⁴ˣ3	⁷÷7	1	4
2	5	6	4	1	⁷²ˣ3	²¹ˣ7
¹⁴⁺3	²⁴⁵ˣ7	5	2	4	6	1
4	⁶ˣ1	7	⁶⁰ˣ6	2	5	3
7	2	3	⁵÷1	5	²⁻4	6

420

⁴²ˣ2	7	¹⁶⁺3	¹⁵⁺5	6	⁴÷1	4
3	²⁴ˣ1	6	4	⁷⁰ˣ5	2	7
6	4	7	¹1	2	³3	⁶⁰ˣ5
⁴÷4	³⁰ˣ2	⁶⁻1	7	⁷²ˣ3	²⁻5	6
1	3	5	6	4	7	2
¹⁷⁵ˣ5	¹¹⁺6	2	3	²⁸ˣ7	4	¹⁰⁺1
7	5	²÷4	2	1	6	3

421

7÷ 7	1	252× 3	2÷ 2	4	180× 6	5
13+ 1	7	4	3	14+ 2	5	6
4	2− 3	5	294× 7	6	1	2− 2
6	2	7	1	5÷ 5	294× 3	4
150× 3	48× 4	6	12+ 5	1	2	7
5	6	2	4	3	7	84× 1
2	5	5− 1	6	7	4	3

422

1− 4	5	168× 7	2÷ 2	3	6	1− 1
252× 7	3	4	5	6	1	2
3	6	2	7÷ 7	1	1− 5	4
5− 6	11+ 7	1	96× 3	4	2	21+ 5
1	2	180× 5	4	588× 7	3	6
240× 5	1	3	6	2	4	7
2	4	6	5÷ 1	5	7	3

423

2− 5	3	84× 7	1	6	9+ 2	4
6÷ 6	1	2	980× 5	4	7	3
2÷ 4	252× 2	5÷ 1	7	54× 3	6	2− 5
2	6	5	40× 4	1	3	7
11+ 1	7	3	252× 6	5	3− 4	60× 2
7	19+ 5	4	3	2	1	6
3	4	6	2	7	5	1

424

180× 3	5	80× 4	84× 6	2	7÷ 7	1
2	4	5	9+ 3	7	16+ 1	6
6	3	2	1	4	5	168× 7
2− 5	3÷ 6	168× 1	7	3	2	4
7	2	6	4	2− 1	3	180× 5
18+ 1	7	50× 3	5	2− 6	4	2
4÷ 4	1	7	2	5	6	3

425

³⁰ˣ 5	¹⁶⁸ˣ 2	7	¹³⁺ 1	4	3	⁵⁸⁸ˣ 6
6	1	3	4	5	7	2
¹⁻ 4	²÷ 3	6	³⁺ 2	1	⁴²⁰ˣ 5	7
3	⁴÷ 4	1	6	7	2	⁴⁻ 5
⁹⁸ˣ 2	7	¹⁸⁰ˣ 5	3	¹⁵⁺ 6	4	1
7	6	2	⁷⁰⁰ˣ 5	3	⁶÷ 1	¹⁻ 4
1	5	4	7	2	6	3

426

³⁻ 2	5	⁴÷ 1	¹²⁺ 3	4	²⁹⁴ˣ 6	7
⁶⁺ 5	1	4	2	3	7	¹⁸⁺ 6
³⁻ 4	¹⁶⁸ˣ 3	7	¹⁸⁰ˣ 6	²÷ 2	1	5
7	2	6	5	1	3	4
¹⁰⁺ 6	4	²⁵²ˣ 3	7	¹⁴⁰ˣ 5	¹⁻ 2	1
1	6	2	4	7	¹²⁰ˣ 5	3
3	¹²⁺ 7	5	⁶÷ 1	6	4	2

427

⁶⁻ 1	⁷²ˣ 6	3	4	⁷⁰ˣ 5	7	¹²⁰ˣ 2
7	²⁻ 4	⁵⁻ 1	6	2	5	3
¹⁵⁰ˣ 5	2	¹⁹⁺ 7	3	1	¹²⁰ˣ 6	4
2	3	5	7	²÷ 6	4	1
⁵⁰⁴ˣ 6	7	²⁻ 4	2	3	¹⁷⁺ 1	5
4	¹⁵⁰ˣ 5	2	⁷÷ 1	7	3	6
3	1	6	5	²÷ 4	2	7

428

⁴÷ 1	¹⁻ 3	2	²¹⁰ˣ 5	¹⁶⁺ 6	7	¹⁷⁺ 4
4	1	6	7	⁷⁵ˣ 5	3	2
²⁹⁴ˣ 2	7	²¹⁰ˣ 1	²÷ 4	3	5	6
3	6	7	2	⁴÷ 4	1	5
7	5	¹⁸⁰ˣ 3	6	2	²⁴ˣ 4	¹⁷⁺ 1
¹⁻ 6	²⁻ 4	5	3	1	2	7
5	2	¹²⁺ 4	1	7	6	3

429

⁶⁷²ˣ 6	4	¹⁻ 1	2	⁵²⁵ˣ 5	3	7
4	²¹⁰ˣ 6	¹⁶⁸ˣ 3	7	²÷ 1	2	5
7	1	4	⁸⁺ 3	2	¹²⁰ˣ 5	6
5	7	2	¹⁵⁰ˣ 6	3	²¹⁺ 4	1
¹⁻ 2	3	5	1	6	7	4
²⁻ 1	³⁻ 2	¹¹⁷⁶ˣ 7	5	4	²÷ 6	3
3	5	6	4	7	²÷ 1	2

430

¹⁻ 3	³⁻ 4	7	⁵÷ 5	1	³÷ 6	2
4	²¹⁰ˣ 7	¹⁻ 2	3	²⁵²ˣ 6	¹⁰⁺ 1	5
²²⁺ 7	5	6	1	2	¹⁸⁺ 4	3
5	6	4	7	3	2	1
¹⁸ˣ 6	3	¹¹⁺ 1	2	4	5	7
1	¹⁸⁰ˣ 2	3	4	²⁴⁵ˣ 5	7	¹³⁺ 6
²÷ 2	1	5	6	7	3	4

431

²÷ 4	2	¹⁰⁵ˣ 7	¹⁸⁹⁰ˣ 3	5	6	²⁸ˣ 1
²²⁺ 6	¹⁻ 4	3	5	7	1	2
1	5	¹⁸⁰ˣ 6	²÷ 4	3	2	7
3	6	5	2	⁶⁰⁴⁸⁰ˣ 1	7	4
2	7	²÷ 1	¹³⁺ 6	¹⁻ 4	5	3
²⁻ 7	3	2	1	6	4	5
5	¹²⁺ 1	4	7	2	3	6

432

²÷ 2	1	¹⁵⁺ 4	5	6	⁴⁻ 3	7
¹⁵⁺ 4	³÷ 2	¹⁻ 7	6	⁷⁺ 3	³⁴⁺ 1	²⁻ 5
7	6	⁷⁰ˣ 2	²ˣ 1	4	5	3
3	7	5	2	1	6	4
1	⁴⁵ˣ 5	3	²⁸ˣ 4	7	2	6
⁸⁶⁴⁰⁰ˣ 6	3	⁷÷ 1	7	5	4	2
5	4	6	3	2	7	1

433

20+ 2	6	5	7	1− 4	3	21× 1
30+ 5	2÷ 4	3÷ 2	6	3÷ 1	7	3
6	2	28× 7	2520× 1	3	5	2− 4
1	2− 5	4	3	7	6	2
3	7	5− 1	4	50× 5	15+ 2	6
4	3	6	5	2	21+ 1	7
7	1	3	2	6	4	5

434

10+ 3	3− 4	1	30+ 2	5	6	7÷ 7
2	5	1− 6	7	2÷ 4	3	1
15× 1	3	5	10+ 6	2	7	96× 4
5	8× 2	3	1	7	4	6
4	1	20160× 7	3	6	20× 5	2
294× 6	7	4	5	3÷ 1	2	9+ 3
7	6	2	4	3	1	5

435

70× 7	80× 5	4	3÷ 3	1	84× 2	6
5	4	4− 1	36× 2	3	6	7
2	3÷ 6	5	3− 4	7	2− 1	3
2÷ 6	2	29+ 3	5	896× 4	7	1
3	11+ 1	7	6	19+ 2	5	4
12+ 1	3	6	7	5	4	2
4	7	2	1	6	8+ 3	5

436

1− 3	2	5× 1	24+ 6	7	4	54000× 5
2− 2	1	5	7	4	6	3
4	27+ 6	2	3	5	17+ 1	7
1	7	2÷ 6	5	2	3	4
7	4	3	1	2÷ 6	10× 5	2
90× 6	2− 5	7	32× 4	3	2	6× 1
5	3	4	2	7÷ 1	7	6

359

437

30× 3	5	13+ 6	7	6720× 2	6+ 1	3360× 4
2	42× 3	7	6	4	5	1
6÷ 6	2	5÷ 5	1	7	4	3
1	504× 6	3	4	5	7	2
7	4	1	3− 2	108× 3	6	5
24+ 4	2÷ 1	2	5	6	1− 3	1− 7
5	7	4	3	1	2	6

438

11+ 2	3	6÷ 1	6	2− 5	14+ 7	4
14+ 1	6	2÷ 2	4	7	50× 5	3
7	4× 1	5400× 4	3	6	2	5
6	4	3	5	336× 2	1	7
4− 3	7	5	2016× 2	1	4	6
700× 5	4− 2	6	7	4	3÷ 3	1
4	5	7	1	3	6	2

439

3528× 7	432× 4	6	2	2− 3	1	10080× 5
6	7	3	1	12+ 5	2	4
2	6	1	3	2÷ 4	5	7
8+ 3	2÷ 1	2− 7	1− 5	2	4	6
4	2	5	6	21× 1	7	3
1	75× 5	17+ 4	7	252× 6	3	2÷ 2
5	3	2	4	7	6	1

440

2520× 7	1	6	5	2	3− 4	90720× 3
360× 4	3	2	6	1	7	5
3	5	4÷ 1	4	7	6	2
1	196× 7	7+ 5	2	6	3	4
13+ 2	4	63× 7	3	5÷ 5	1	6× 6
6	2− 2	4	7	3	14+ 5	1
5	3− 6	3	4÷ 1	4	2	7

441

$^{105\times}$7	$^{10+}$3	5	2	$^{17+}$4	$^{6\div}$1	6
3	5	$^{3-}$1	7	6	4	$^{2-}$2
$^{2\div}$2	1	4	$^{24+}$5	$^{540\times}$3	6	$^{1-}$7
$^{28224\times}$6	7	2	1	5	3	4
4	2	7	6	1	$^{175\times}$5	3
$^{30\times}$1	6	3	4	2	7	5
5	$^{13+}$4	6	3	7	$^{2\div}$2	1

442

$^{7\div}$7	1	$^{2-}$6	4	$^{1-}$3	2	$^{30\times}$5
$^{36\times}$3	$^{175\times}$5	7	$^{2\div}$2	4	1	6
6	2	5	1	$^{30+}$7	4	$^{14+}$3
$^{43200\times}$5	$^{42\times}$7	2	3	1	6	4
2	4	1	5	6	3	7
$^{3-}$1	3	4	$^{84\times}$6	5	7	$^{2\div}$2
4	6	3	7	2	5	1

443

$^{4-}$7	$^{1152\times}$4	2	3	1	6	$^{1225\times}$5
3	$^{72000\times}$6	5	$^{28+}$4	2	1	7
6	2	3	5	4	7	$^{2\div}$1
4	7	1	$^{2\div}$6	3	5	2
5	3	4	$^{6-}$1	$^{42\times}$7	2	$^{13+}$6
2	1	$^{84\times}$6	7	$^{15+}$5	3	4
1	5	7	2	6	4	3

444

$^{36288\times}$6	$^{7875\times}$3	5	$^{2\div}$4	2	$^{6-}$7	$^{2\div}$1
4	5	7	3	$^{24\times}$6	1	2
2	$^{5-}$6	1	5	4	$^{15\times}$3	$^{3-}$7
3	7	6	2	1	5	4
$^{8+}$1	2	3	$^{294\times}$6	7	$^{35+}$4	5
5	$^{12+}$1	$^{2\div}$4	7	3	2	6
7	4	2	1	5	6	3

445

29+ 1	7	6	3	5	2− 2	4
7	28800× 1	4	70× 5	2	2÷ 6	3
72× 4	3	20× 2	7	27+ 1	2− 5	6
6	4	5	2	7	3	1
3	2	3− 7	4	6	1	5
5	6	3÷ 3	4÷ 1	4	3− 7	9+ 2
2	5	1	9+ 6	3	4	7

446

12+ 2	4	6	12600× 3	5	22+ 1	7
4	3	5	2	7	6	1
2÷ 3	7	13440× 1	5	2	4	84× 6
6	25× 5	3	4÷ 1	4	7	2
5	1	7	3− 6	3	40× 2	4
1	2	4	3− 7	6÷ 6	5	11+ 3
1− 7	6	2	4	1	3	5

447

10+ 6	3	28× 7	4	6÷ 1	11+ 5	2
98× 7	1	2700× 5	2	6	4	52920× 3
2	7	6	3	5	1	4
12× 4	2520× 6	5÷ 1	5	3	4− 2	7
1	4	3	7	12+ 2	6	5
3	5	2− 2	6	4	7	1
3− 5	2	4	7÷ 1	7	3	6

448

11+ 3	4÷ 1	4	21+ 5	6	28× 2	7
7	4	5	1	2÷ 3	6	2
1	60× 6	2	63504× 3	245× 7	5	1− 4
2− 4	5	1	6	2	7	3
2	7	3	24+ 4	5	6÷ 1	6
10× 5	2	6	7	4	3	1
3− 6	3	7	2	20× 1	4	5

449

2÷ 1	2	9+ 7	6	29+ 5	14+ 4	3
15120× 5	6	2	4	1	3	7
6	4÷ 1	4	3	7	5	10+ 2
7	3	75× 5	1	4	2	6
45360× 2	4	3	5	3÷ 6	9+ 7	1
3	5	6	7	2	1	1- 4
3- 4	7	1	2	3	6	5

450

2- 7	75600× 5	1	6	13+ 4	8+ 3	2
5	11+ 4	6	6+ 1	7	2	3
6	1	4	3	2	35× 7	140× 5
2- 2	2÷ 6	3	6- 7	1	5	4
4	3	5	3÷ 2	6	1	7
3÷ 3	140× 2	7	20× 4	5	432× 6	1
1	7	2	5	3	4	6

451

17 4	7	6 5	1	11 8	3	11 6	10 2
19 8	6	14 3	4	17 7	2	1	5
6	5	8 2	7	4 1	8	4	3
1 1	2	4	7 5	3	21 6	7	8
12 5	15 8	6	2	17 4	11 1	3	7
7	10 3	1	8	5	14 4	2	11 6
3	4	18 7	8 6	2	17 5	8	1
3 2	1	8	3	6 6	7	5	4

452

10 2	7 4	11 1	6	8 3	5	22 7	8
5	2	4	9 3	6	8	6 1	7
3	1	6	17 8	23 7	2	5 5	7 4
18 6	5	7	4	8	3	14 2	1
7	13 6	13 3	10 1	5	4	8	2
12 8	7	2	8 5	4	10 1	3	6
4	12 3	8	2	1	13 7	6	8 5
1	8	5 5	9 7	2	10 6	4	3

453

5	1	3	7	4	8	6	2
4	6	2	3	1	7	8	5
3	4	1	2	8	5	7	6
1	3	7	8	6	2	5	4
7	2	8	6	5	4	1	3
8	5	6	1	2	3	4	7
2	8	5	4	7	6	3	1
6	7	4	5	3	1	2	8

454

1	6	2	7	5	8	4	3
5	1	6	8	7	3	2	4
8	5	1	4	3	6	7	2
7	8	4	3	2	1	6	5
6	3	8	2	4	7	5	1
2	4	7	1	6	5	3	8
4	7	3	5	8	2	1	6
3	2	5	6	1	4	8	7

455

7	4	2	5	3	1	6	8
6	2	3	1	4	5	8	7
2	8	7	6	5	4	3	1
4	7	6	8	1	2	5	3
8	3	1	4	6	7	2	5
3	5	4	7	2	8	1	6
1	6	5	2	8	3	7	4
5	1	8	3	7	6	4	2

456

2	1	4	6	3	5	7	8
3	4	6	1	7	2	8	5
8	2	3	5	1	7	6	4
1	6	5	4	8	3	2	7
4	5	7	8	6	1	3	2
5	3	8	7	2	4	1	6
6	7	2	3	4	8	5	1
7	8	1	2	5	6	4	3

457

8	4	1	6	3	5	7	2
4	8	2	1	6	7	5	3
5	1	3	7	2	6	8	4
2	7	8	4	5	3	6	1
3	6	5	8	1	4	2	7
7	3	6	2	4	8	1	5
6	2	4	5	7	1	3	8
1	5	7	3	8	2	4	6

458

8	2	4	5	6	7	1	3
4	7	5	1	3	8	2	6
6	3	7	2	8	1	4	5
5	1	3	8	7	4	6	2
1	5	2	3	4	6	7	8
2	8	6	4	1	5	3	7
7	4	8	6	2	3	5	1
3	6	1	7	5	2	8	4

459

2	5	4	6	7	1	8	3
3	8	5	7	4	2	6	1
5	7	6	4	3	8	1	2
1	4	3	8	2	7	5	6
8	1	7	2	6	4	3	5
7	6	1	3	8	5	2	4
6	2	8	5	1	3	4	7
4	3	2	1	5	6	7	8

460

3	7	6	8	1	5	2	4
5	4	8	6	2	1	3	7
2	3	7	4	6	8	5	1
6	2	5	1	8	4	7	3
4	6	1	2	3	7	8	5
7	5	2	3	4	6	1	8
8	1	3	5	7	2	4	6
1	8	4	7	5	3	6	2

461

6	4	7	2	8	3	1	5
3	2	8	7	5	4	6	1
2	1	5	6	7	8	3	4
5	6	3	8	1	7	4	2
8	7	1	4	2	6	5	3
7	3	4	5	6	1	2	8
1	5	6	3	4	2	8	7
4	8	2	1	3	5	7	6

462

8	4	6	2	3	1	5	7
3	1	2	5	6	4	7	8
4	5	3	1	7	2	8	6
1	7	8	3	4	5	6	2
7	2	4	6	5	8	1	3
5	6	7	8	1	3	2	4
2	3	5	7	8	6	4	1
6	8	1	4	2	7	3	5

463

4	7	1	8	3	6	5	2
6	1	3	4	2	7	8	5
2	8	4	6	1	5	7	3
1	3	6	2	5	8	4	7
5	4	8	7	6	3	2	1
3	6	7	5	8	2	1	4
8	2	5	1	7	4	3	6
7	5	2	3	4	1	6	8

464

2	4	7	1	5	3	6	8
8	6	4	3	1	5	2	7
1	5	3	2	6	8	7	4
5	7	6	4	2	1	8	3
3	8	1	5	7	2	4	6
6	1	2	7	8	4	3	5
4	2	8	6	3	7	5	1
7	3	5	8	4	6	1	2

465

8	3	2	4	7	1	5	6
1	4	8	5	6	7	2	3
5	2	1	8	3	6	7	4
7	1	4	6	8	5	3	2
6	5	3	7	2	4	8	1
2	8	7	1	4	3	6	5
4	7	6	3	5	2	1	8
3	6	5	2	1	8	4	7

466

2	5	8	7	6	3	1	4
6	4	5	3	8	1	2	7
8	1	7	5	2	4	3	6
4	2	3	8	5	7	6	1
5	3	4	6	1	8	7	2
7	8	6	1	4	2	5	3
3	6	1	2	7	5	4	8
1	7	2	4	3	6	8	5

467

6	7	5	1	8	2	4	3
8	5	1	6	2	4	3	7
3	6	4	5	7	8	1	2
7	2	3	4	6	5	8	1
4	8	6	2	1	3	7	5
1	3	2	8	5	7	6	4
5	4	8	7	3	1	2	6
2	1	7	3	4	6	5	8

468

1	3	8	5	6	7	2	4
8	1	7	6	4	5	3	2
7	5	3	1	2	4	8	6
4	8	5	2	3	6	7	1
6	7	2	4	8	3	1	5
2	4	6	8	7	1	5	3
3	6	1	7	5	2	4	8
5	2	4	3	1	8	6	7

469

6	7	5	1	3	8	4	2
3	2	6	4	5	7	8	1
2	5	8	3	7	1	6	4
8	3	4	7	6	2	1	5
7	4	1	2	8	6	5	3
5	1	2	8	4	3	7	6
4	8	3	6	1	5	2	7
1	6	7	5	2	4	3	8

470

5	7	4	3	6	8	2	1
8	2	1	7	4	6	5	3
4	1	6	5	8	7	3	2
6	4	7	8	2	3	1	5
3	8	2	1	5	4	7	6
1	6	3	2	7	5	8	4
7	3	5	4	1	2	6	8
2	5	8	6	3	1	4	7

471

4	7	8	5	6	2	3	1
7	1	3	2	4	8	6	5
6	5	1	4	2	7	8	3
1	8	2	7	5	3	4	6
5	3	6	1	7	4	2	8
8	2	5	3	1	6	7	4
3	4	7	6	8	5	1	2
2	6	4	8	3	1	5	7

472

4	6	1	3	2	8	5	7
2	3	5	6	1	4	7	8
8	7	3	1	6	2	4	5
7	5	8	2	4	3	1	6
5	2	6	4	8	7	3	1
3	1	2	8	7	5	6	4
1	8	4	7	5	6	2	3
6	4	7	5	3	1	8	2

473

3	4	1	2	6	7	8	5
4	2	6	3	5	1	7	8
5	3	2	6	7	8	4	1
1	7	8	5	4	2	6	3
7	5	4	1	8	6	3	2
2	6	7	8	1	3	5	4
8	1	5	7	3	4	2	6
6	8	3	4	2	5	1	7

474

2	3	5	6	4	7	8	1
4	2	8	1	7	5	6	3
3	7	2	4	1	8	5	6
1	6	7	8	5	3	4	2
6	5	1	2	3	4	7	8
7	8	3	5	6	1	2	4
5	4	6	3	8	2	1	7
8	1	4	7	2	6	3	5

475

2	4	3	1	8	5	7	6
3	7	5	4	6	2	1	8
7	8	6	2	3	1	5	4
6	3	8	5	4	7	2	1
4	2	1	3	5	8	6	7
8	5	2	7	1	6	4	3
1	6	7	8	2	4	3	5
5	1	4	6	7	3	8	2

476

4	8	7	5	1	2	3	6
2	3	8	1	5	4	6	7
5	6	1	7	8	3	2	4
7	4	2	6	3	1	5	8
3	2	5	4	7	6	8	1
6	1	3	8	2	7	4	5
8	7	4	2	6	5	1	3
1	5	6	3	4	8	7	2

477

8	1	2	4	7	3	5	6
3	5	7	1	2	4	6	8
1	4	3	5	6	2	8	7
4	8	6	2	1	7	3	5
5	2	4	6	3	8	7	1
2	7	8	3	5	6	1	4
6	3	1	7	8	5	4	2
7	6	5	8	4	1	2	3

478

5	1	8	7	4	2	6	3
7	3	5	2	1	6	8	4
4	2	3	1	6	8	5	7
3	6	7	8	5	4	2	1
8	5	1	6	3	7	4	2
1	8	6	4	2	3	7	5
2	7	4	5	8	1	3	6
6	4	2	3	7	5	1	8

479

3	6	4	5	7	1	8	2
1	4	8	6	3	2	5	7
7	5	1	8	4	3	2	6
5	8	6	7	2	4	3	1
2	7	5	3	6	8	1	4
8	1	7	2	5	6	4	3
4	3	2	1	8	7	6	5
6	2	3	4	1	5	7	8

480

3	7	4	8	6	1	2	5
4	1	7	3	2	8	5	6
2	8	5	4	7	6	3	1
5	4	6	7	1	2	8	3
6	2	1	5	4	3	7	8
8	6	2	1	3	5	4	7
1	3	8	2	5	7	6	4
7	5	3	6	8	4	1	2

481

[168]7	[60]5	2	[48]1	8	6	[84]4	3
8	3	6	[120]4	5	[2]2	7	[1]1
[8]4	[84]7	3	6	[84]2	1	[320]8	5
1	[240]6	4	[6]2	7	[105]3	5	8
2	8	5	3	6	7	[28]1	4
[48]6	2	[40]1	5	[96]4	8	3	7
[15]3	4	8	[21]7	1	[40]5	2	[72]6
5	[56]1	7	8	3	4	6	2

482

[72]3	4	[2]2	6	[48]8	7	[28]5	[40]1
6	[56]7	[90]5	1	[42]2	4	3	[6]8
[160]5	8	6	3	7	2	1	[56]4
8	[60]6	3	[20]5	4	1	2	7
4	5	[56]7	2	[30]1	6	[144]8	3
[7]1	2	4	[96]8	3	5	[84]7	6
7	1	8	[56]4	[90]5	3	6	2
[6]2	3	1	7	6	[160]8	4	5

483

[112]7	2	[120]8	[24]4	6	1	[15]5	3
8	5	3	[7]1	7	[40]4	[60]2	6
[72]3	6	4	[144]8	1	2	[7]7	5
[60]4	3	[56]7	6	[56]2	5	1	[64]8
5	8	1	3	4	7	[18]6	2
[12]1	[210]7	6	[42]2	[240]5	8	3	4
2	[8]4	5	7	3	6	[56]8	1
6	1	2	[5]5	[96]8	3	4	7

484

[240]5	[24]2	3	7	1	[120]6	4	[48]8
8	6	4	1	[105]7	3	5	2
[48]2	4	6	[120]8	5	[56]7	[6]1	3
[30]6	[448]8	7	5	4	2	3	[35]1
1	5	8	3	[144]6	[4]4	2	7
[84]4	[3]1	[24]2	6	3	8	[210]7	5
7	3	1	2	[16]8	5	6	[192]4
3	[140]7	5	4	2	1	8	6

485

³1	³⁰3	2	¹⁶⁸4	6	7	¹⁶⁰5	8
3	5	⁴⁸6	1	¹²2	¹¹²8	7	4
²⁴⁵5	7	8	6	1	2	¹²4	3
7	⁶2	1	3	¹¹²8	¹²⁰4	6	⁴⁰5
¹⁴⁴6	4	¹⁰⁵3	2	7	5	8	1
¹²⁸8	6	5	7	²⁴4	1	⁶3	2
2	8	⁶⁰4	5	3	6	1	⁸⁴7
⁴4	⁷1	7	¹²⁰8	5	3	2	6

486

⁹⁶8	4	³1	3	⁷⁰2	5	³³⁶6	7
¹⁴2	3	³⁰6	1	5	7	⁴⁸4	8
1	7	⁵5	¹⁶2	8	¹²6	3	4
¹²⁰4	⁴⁰5	⁸⁴3	³⁹²8	7	1	2	⁶⁰6
6	8	4	7	¹⁸1	3	5	2
5	1	7	¹²⁰4	6	⁴⁸2	8	3
³⁶3	6	2	5	⁴⁸4	⁵⁶8	7	1
¹¹²7	2	8	6	3	4	⁵1	5

487

⁴²3	7	⁴⁸6	4	2	²¹⁰5	⁴⁰1	8
¹⁵1	2	⁸⁴3	¹⁹²8	4	7	6	5
5	3	4	7	6	⁶⁴8	⁶2	1
⁹⁶8	6	⁷7	³⁵1	5	2	4	3
2	¹⁵5	1	3	7	⁶⁰4	¹⁹²8	6
⁵⁶7	8	⁹⁶2	6	¹⁸1	3	5	4
⁹⁶4	1	8	⁵⁰5	3	6	⁹⁸7	2
6	4	5	2	²⁴8	1	3	7

488

⁸⁰2	⁵⁶7	4	²⁰⁰5	8	³⁶6	¹²1	3
8	2	⁴²3	7	5	1	6	4
5	¹²1	6	2	²⁸4	¹²⁰8	³3	¹¹²7
¹⁴⁴6	4	2	1	7	3	5	8
⁹⁶4	6	²⁴8	3	⁴²1	⁷⁰5	7	2
3	8	1	⁴⁸4	6	7	2	³⁰5
³⁵7	¹⁰⁵3	5	6	2	¹²⁸4	8	1
1	5	7	⁴⁸8	3	2	4	6

489

120 5	8	1	288 6	168 4	7	2	3
7 1	7	3	4	6	2	40 8	5
252 6	560 5	7	2	18 1	480 4	3	8
7	2	210 6	8	3	1	5	112 4
96 8	3	5	1	2	560 6	4	7
3	1	4	7	5	48 8	6	70 2
192 4	6	240 2	3	8	5	7	1
2	4	8	5	7	18 3	1	6

490

420 5	2	7	120 8	1	3	576 6	96 4
2352 7	6	15 1	5	4	8	3	2
8	3	5	28 4	7	1	2	6
6	7	240 3	1	320 2	4	5	8
96 1	8	2	105 7	5	240 6	4	168 3
4	5	8	216 6	3	2	7	1
3	32 1	4	2	336 6	5	8	35 7
2	4	6	3	8	7	1	5

491

140 5	12 4	1	84 7	6	2	120 3	192 8
2	7	3	420 4	5	1	8	6
576 8	2	180 6	5	3	336 7	4	1
4	6	5	3	7	8	8 1	2
126 7	3	2	1536 8	1	6	525 5	4
1	8	4	6	120 2	3	7	5
6	35 5	7	1	512 8	4	84 2	3
3	1	8	2	4	5	6	7

492

384 8	21 3	7	30 6	2 1	120 2	4	5
6	4	8 8	1	2	3	840 5	7
168 3	2	1	56 5	48 7	6	8	4
1	8	180 3	2	4	200 5	14 7	6
7	420 6	4	3	5	8	2	1
2	7	5	192 4	8	1	6	48 3
5	40 1	2	336 7	72 6	4	21 3	8
4	5	6	8	3	7	1	2

493

1 ⁽⁸⁾	7 ⁽⁴⁴⁸⁾	8	3 ⁽²¹⁶⁾	4	6	2 ⁽⁶⁰⁾	5
2	8	5 ⁽⁶⁰⁾	4	1 ⁽¹⁶⁸⁾	3	7 ⁽²¹⁰⁾	6
4	2 ⁽⁸⁰⁾	3	7	8	5	6	1
8	5	1	6 ⁽⁵⁷⁶⁾	3	7 ⁽¹⁶⁸⁾	4	2
5 ⁽³⁵⁾	1	7 ⁽²⁵²⁾	2	6	8	3	4 ⁽⁶⁷²⁾
7	4 ⁽⁴⁾	6	1 ⁽¹⁴⁰⁾	5	2 ⁽¹⁶⁾	8	3
6 ⁽⁴³²⁾	3	2	5 ⁽⁴⁰⁾	7	4	1	8
3	6	4	8	2 ⁽¹⁰⁾	1	5	7

$$493$$

494

7 ⁽¹¹²⁾	2	3 ⁽⁶⁷²⁾	4 ⁽³⁶⁰⁾	6 ⁽⁷²⁰⁾	8	5	1 ⁽⁹⁶⁾
4 ⁽¹²⁰⁾	8	7	6	5	1 ⁽⁴²⁾	3	2
1	5	4	8	3	2	7	6
6	7 ⁽¹⁷⁵⁾	1	5	2 ⁽⁵⁶⁰⁾	3	4 ⁽²⁸⁸⁾	8
2 ⁽²⁴⁰⁾	4 ⁽¹⁹²⁾	5	1 ⁽²⁾	8	7	6	3
3	6	8	2	7 ⁽²⁹⁴⁾	5	1 ⁽⁷⁰⁾	4
8	3 ⁽¹⁸⁾	6	7	1	4 ⁽⁷⁶⁸⁾	2	5
5	1	2	3	4	6	8	7

495

8 ⁽¹²⁸⁰⁾	4 ⁽⁴⁰⁾	2	5	6 ⁽¹²⁶⁾	7	3	1
4	8	6 ⁽¹⁰⁸⁾	1	2 ⁽⁴⁰⁾	5	7 ⁽¹⁶⁸⁾	3
5	7 ⁽¹⁶⁸⁾	3	6	1	2 ⁽²⁸⁸⁾	4	8 ⁽⁴⁰⁾
6 ⁽⁷²⁾	1	7 ⁽³⁹²⁾	8	4	3	2	5
2	3	8	7	5 ⁽⁸⁴⁰⁾	6	1 ⁽¹²⁰⁾	4
1	6	4 ⁽⁸⁰⁾	3	7	8	5	2 ⁽⁶⁷²⁾
3 ⁽²¹⁰⁾	2	5	4	8	1 ⁽²⁴⁾	6	7
7	5	1	2	3	4	8	6

496

4 ⁽⁷²⁾	6	3	2 ⁽²⁴⁰⁾	5	1 ⁽⁴⁸⁾	8	7 ⁽¹⁴⁰⁾
7 ⁽³⁵⁾	1	8	3	2 ⁽²⁾	6	4	5
5	7 ⁽⁵⁶⁾	2 ⁽¹⁰⁾	6 ⁽¹⁴⁴⁾	1	8 ⁽⁶⁷²⁾	3 ⁽³⁶⁾	4
1	8	5	4	6	2	7	3
3 ⁽¹⁴⁴⁾	2	4 ⁽²⁴⁾	7 ⁽²⁸⁰⁾	8	5 ⁽⁴⁰⁾	6	1
8	3	6	5	7 ⁽⁵⁸⁸⁾	4	1	2
2 ⁽⁴⁸⁾	4	1	8 ⁽²⁸⁰⁾	3	7	5 ⁽²⁴⁰⁾	6 ⁽⁶⁾
6	5	7	1	4	3	2	8

497

[16] 2	[160] 5	8	7	3	[42] 4	1	[30] 6
8	[36] 3	4	2	[112] 7	[30] 1	6	5
1	4	3	8	2	6	[70] 5	7
[4] 4	1	[2352] 7	6	[336] 8	5	2	[144] 3
[40] 5	8	1	4	6	7	3	2
[1512] 6	7	2	1	[7200] 5	3	4	8
3	2	6	5	4	[53760] 8	7	1
7	6	5	3	1	2	8	4

498

[24] 6	[4032] 3	4	7	[10] 2	5	1	[160] 8
1	8	3	2	[84] 7	6	4	5
4	[40] 5	[56] 8	[30] 6	1	2	[126] 7	3
8	1	7	5	[36] 4	3	6	[6720] 2
[105] 5	[480] 4	1	[192] 8	3	7	2	6
7	6	2	3	8	[4] 4	5	1
3	2	5	4	[24] 6	[240] 1	8	[84] 7
[14] 2	7	6	1	5	8	3	4

499

[90] 6	8	2	[9000] 5	[168] 3	4	7	[12] 1
[168] 8	3	1	4	5	[7] 7	2	6
7	[84] 6	5	3	[4] 4	[6720] 1	8	2
[80] 4	2	7	6	1	5	3	8
5	4	[12] 3	1	[2304] 2	[48] 8	6	7
[14] 2	1	4	[112] 7	8	[450] 6	5	3
[5040] 1	7	8	2	6	3	4	5
3	5	6	8	7	2	[4] 1	4

500

[30] 2	5	[168] 8	3	7	[20] 4	1	[48] 6
3	[47040] 6	[64] 2	4	8	5	[210] 7	1
4	7	[54] 3	[10] 1	2	6	5	8
7	3	6	[10] 2	5	[16] 1	8	[72] 4
8	[92160] 4	[7] 7	5	[32] 1	2	6	3
5	2	1	6	4	8	[42] 3	7
6	1	5	8	[84] 3	7	4	2
1	8	[168] 4	7	6	[30] 3	2	5

501

6	4	2	3	1	5	8	7
1	2	3	7	6	4	5	8
7	1	8	5	3	2	4	6
4	3	5	8	7	6	2	1
2	7	4	6	5	8	1	3
3	5	7	2	8	1	6	4
5	8	6	1	4	7	3	2
8	6	1	4	2	3	7	5

502

4	5	8	2	7	1	6	3
8	7	5	3	2	6	4	1
6	1	7	4	8	5	3	2
5	2	3	6	1	4	7	8
1	8	6	7	4	3	2	5
2	3	4	8	5	7	1	6
3	4	1	5	6	2	8	7
7	6	2	1	3	8	5	4

503

2	1	4	5	7	8	3	6
3	2	1	4	8	7	6	5
4	5	8	7	3	6	1	2
5	3	6	1	4	2	7	8
6	7	3	2	5	1	8	4
8	4	5	6	1	3	2	7
1	6	7	8	2	4	5	3
7	8	2	3	6	5	4	1

504

2	5	8	1	3	4	7	6
4	3	6	7	5	2	8	1
6	2	7	4	1	8	5	3
7	4	1	5	2	6	3	8
5	7	3	6	8	1	2	4
8	1	4	2	7	3	6	5
3	6	5	8	4	7	1	2
1	8	2	3	6	5	4	7

505

96	56			24	90		
2	8	7	1	4	5	6	3
8	2016 2	6	280 7	3	1	20 5	4
6	4	8	5	2	7	24 3	1
3	7	2	120 6	5	4	1	8
35 7	3 3	1	4032 4	6	4608 8	2	210 5
5	1	11520 4	3	8	2	7	6
1	5	3	8	7	6	56 4	2
4	6	10 5	2	1	3	8	7

506

48	30	6720			8	96	
6	5	2	7	1	8	4	3
2	6	3	5	20 4	1	84 7	8
4	56 8	5	1	42 3	7	2	6
7	1	8	4	2	42 3	120 6	5
24 8	3	1	18 6	7	2	9600 5	4
60 5	2	6	3	8	4	1	56 7
21 3	7	112 4	2	5	6	8	1
1	4	7	48 8	6	30 5	3	2

507

2	48			42		50400	
1	2	8	3	7	6	5	4
2	48 1	280 5	8	4	3	6	7
6	8	54 3	7	640 1	5	40 4	2
60 4	3	6	1	8	42 7	2	5
5	28 7	4	60 6	2	8	3	24 1
3	192 6	1	2	5	56 4	7	8
8	4	1008 7	5	6	2	48 1	3
35 7	5	2	4	3	1	8	6

508

120		42	168			16	
5	3	1	7	6	4	2	8
8	7	6	12 3	20 5	2	1	48 4
24 1	224 8	7	4	2	75 5	3	6
6	4	25200 3	8	1	56 7	5	2
4	1	5	2	7	8	72 6	3
12 2	6	80 8	5	3	1	4	35 7
42 7	5	2	24 6	192 4	168 3	8	1
3	2	4	1	8	6	7	5

509

8 [224]	7 [210]	6	5	1 [8]	4	2 [30]	3
7	4	3 [24]	8	2	1 [2]	5	6 [252]
3 [120]	8	5	1 [80640]	4	2	6	7
2 [3360]	5	4	7	6	8	3 [24]	1
6 [30]	1	7	2	5	3	4	8
5	2	1	3	7 [210]	6	8 [15680]	4
1	6 [72]	8 [96]	4	3	5	7	2
4	3	2 [96]	6	8	7	1	5

510

2 [30]	5 [320]	8	4 [8]	3 [1080]	6	1 [42]	7
5	8	1	2	6	4	7 [168]	3
3	2 [42]	4 [140]	7 [336]	5	1	8	6 [48]
1 [48]	7	5	6	8	3	2	4
6	3	7	1 [40320]	2	5 [140]	4	8 [16]
8	1 [12]	3	5	4	7	6 [90]	2
4 [112]	6	2	3	7	8	5	1 [5]
7	4	6 [48]	8	1	2	3	5

511

8 [5−]	6 [16+]	4 [1−]	2 [7+]	5	1 [2−]	3	7 [12+]
3	2	5	7 [3−]	8 [18+]	6	1	4
1 [1]	8	6 [3−]	4	7	3	5 [7+]	2
4 [3−]	1	3	8 [2−]	2 [1−]	7	6 [13+]	5 [5]
2 [7+]	4	1	6	3	5 [12+]	7	8 [9+]
7 [15+]	5 [3−]	2	3 [11+]	6 [18+]	4	8	1
5	3	7	1	4 [5+]	8 [6−]	2 [8+]	6
6 [1−]	7	8 [13+]	5	1	2	4 [1−]	3

512

3 [12+]	4 [15+]	8	5 [4−]	1	2 [2]	6 [1−]	7
2	7	3	8	4	5 [4−]	1 [13+]	6 [11+]
6 [2−]	3 [8+]	5	1 [13+]	7	8	4	2 [13+]
4	2 [15+]	6	7	5	1 [7−]	8	3
1 [7+]	5	4 [13+]	6	3	7 [13+]	2 [3−]	8
8 [20+]	1	7 [6−]	3 [7+]	2	6	5	4 [10+]
7	8 [14+]	1	2	6 [2−]	4	3 [3]	5
5	6	2 [2−]	4	8 [18+]	3	7	1

513

3−4	7	2−8	6	2	1−3	10+1	13+5
3 3	3+2	2−7	10+1	5	4	6	8
13+8	1	5	3−4	7	2 2	3	14+6
1	4 4−	2	1−7	6	20+8	5	3
4−2	8+3	6	6−8	1 1	5	7	5+4
6	5	10+3	2	3−4	7	10+8	1
1−5	6	4	3	7−8	1	2	9+7
1−7	8	6+1	5	13+3	6	4	2

514

12+7	4−8	4	1−5	1	5+2	5+6	9+3
5	7 7	7−1	6	4	3	6−8	2
4+3	1	8	14+7	6	10+5	2−2	4
14+8	1−3	5	2	7	4	1	10+6
6	2	11+7	4	19+5	8	3	1
7+1	4	10+2	8	14+3	6	2−7	5
2	5	1−6	3	8	1 1	19+4	7
10+4	6	4+3	1	14+2	7	5	8

515

20+7	8	5 5	10+6	1	3	2−4	2
5	10+3	7	1	14+6	10+8	2	2−4
2	5	12+4	1−3	7	1	8 8	6
4+3	2−6	8	4	11+5	15+2	6−7	1
1	4	3−3	6−8	2	7	6	2−5
7−8	1	6	2	4	8+5	3	7
2−6	11+7	2	12+5	3	4	7−1	8
4	2	1 1	15+7	8	6	14+5	3

516

4 4	10 3	7	19+5	3−1	2−8	6	5−2
5−3	8	11+2	6	4	4−1	5	7
4−1	5	4	8	1−7	6	9+2	3
5	13+6	4+1	3	17+8	2	7	4
2−8	2	5	1	4−3	7	8+4	19+6
6	7−1	8	5−7	2−2	4	3	5
7−7	2−4	6	2	5	8+3	1	8
5−2	7	1−3	4	6	5	7−8	1

517

^{2−}5	7	³3	⁶⁺2	4	¹³⁺6	^{6−}8	⁴⁺1
^{3−}7	¹¹⁺4	5	¹⁷⁺8	6	1	2	3
4	2	6	3	^{2−}5	¹⁶⁺7	^{7−}1	8
^{2−}8	⁶⁺1	¹⁷⁺7	6	3	5	4	^{5−}2
6	5	¹1	4	^{6−}8	2	¹⁴⁺3	7
⁴⁺3	¹⁷⁺8	2	7	⁵⁺1	4	6	5
1	¹⁸⁺6	8	¹³⁺5	²2	^{5−}3	^{2−}7	^{2−}4
⁵⁺2	3	4	1	7	8	5	6

518

¹⁵⁺4	¹⁰⁺6	3	1	¹⁰⁺7	¹²⁺5	2	^{2−}8
3	¹⁶⁺8	7	⁴4	1	2	5	6
8	1	^{1−}6	5	¹⁵⁺2	7	¹⁴⁺4	3
¹⁴⁺2	5	¹²⁺4	8	6	^{2−}3	1	7
7	⁵⁺2	⁸8	^{2−}3	5	^{5−}1	6	⁹⁺4
¹²⁺6	3	⁷⁺1	2	4	^{4−}8	¹²⁺7	5
1	¹²⁺7	5	^{2−}6	8	4	3	2
5	⁶⁺4	2	^{4−}7	3	⁶6	8	^{7−}1

519

¹⁵⁺8	5	2	⁴⁺1	3	¹⁸⁺7	6	4
⁹⁺2	²⁶⁺8	7	4	²³⁺6	1	¹³⁺5	⁴⁺3
3	7	5	6	2	4	8	1
4	²⁴⁺6	^{4−}3	7	¹⁷⁺5	8	^{7−}1	^{5−}2
6	4	⁴⁺1	3	8	^{1−}5	⁵⁺2	7
7	1	³⁰⁺8	2	4	6	3	³⁰⁺5
^{4−}1	^{3−}3	6	5	7	⁶⁺2	4	8
5	^{2−}2	4	8	1	3	7	6

520

⁴4	^{6−}2	8	¹²⁺5	⁵⁺3	¹⁸⁺7	1	6
²⁹⁺6	4	5	7	2	3	¹⁶⁺8	1
^{1−}2	3	6	8	²⁰⁺4	1	7	²³⁺5
²⁵⁺7	5	⁴⁺1	6	8	2	3	4
^{7−}8	7	2	1	²³⁺5	4	¹²⁺6	3
1	6	¹⁰⁺3	4	7	^{1−}5	2	8
²⁰⁺5	8	7	3	1	6	4	^{5−}2
⁴⁺3	1	^{2−}4	2	6	^{3−}8	5	7

521

³⁻6	3	²³⁺8	1	²⁰⁺5	2	¹⁻4	¹¹⁺7
³⁰⁺7	6	4	8	2	3	5	1
8	1	²⁴⁺5	¹⁻7	6	4	¹⁻2	3
⁶⁺2	8	1	6	⁴4	²⁻7	3	⁷⁺5
4	7	6	⁴⁺3	1	5	³⁵⁺8	2
⁴⁺1	5	²⁰⁺3	2	8	6	7	¹⁹⁺4
3	¹³⁺4	2	5	7	1	⁷⁺6	8
5	2	¹¹⁺7	4	3	8	1	6

522

¹¹⁺2	4	5	⁴⁻8	⁴⁺3	1	6	¹³⁺7
¹⁸⁺7	²⁻3	¹⁻6	4	¹⁵⁺5	8	2	¹⁻1
8	1	7	¹¹⁺5	²⁰⁺4	⁹⁺6	3	2
3	¹⁷⁺6	1	2	7	5	4	¹⁹⁺8
6	5	3	⁷⁻1	8	⁵⁻2	7	4
¹⁻4	⁶⁻2	²⁴⁺8	3	⁵⁻1	7	²²⁺5	⁶6
5	8	¹⁴⁺2	7	6	⁹⁺4	1	3
1	7	4	6	2	3	8	5

523

²²⁺8	³⁻1	4	¹⁰⁺7	¹⁶⁺5	3	6	¹⁻2
4	5	⁶⁺7	3	¹⁴⁺6	8	2	1
5	⁵⁻2	1	²³⁺4	3	⁶6	²³⁺7	8
¹¹⁺1	7	¹⁻3	2	4	5	8	¹⁴⁺6
6	4	²⁹⁺8	¹⁻1	2	7	3	5
⁵⁻7	6	2	8	³⁻1	4	²⁵⁺5	¹⁴⁺3
2	³⁻3	6	5	8	1	4	7
¹¹⁺3	8	¹⁻5	6	7	2	¹⁻1	4

524

¹⁵⁺2	4	⁷⁻1	8	⁸⁺3	¹³⁺6	¹²⁺5	7
3	⁷⁻8	5	¹⁻1	4	7	⁴⁻2	6
5	1	4	³²⁺6	8	⁶⁻2	¹⁰⁺7	3
1	²⁻3	7	5	6	8	²¹⁺4	⁶⁺2
¹⁻7	5	⁶⁻8	2	⁵⁺1	3	6	4
6	⁷⁺2	3	³⁻4	7	1	8	⁶⁺5
⁴⁻8	²⁹⁺6	2	7	²³⁺5	4	3	1
4	7	6	3	²2	5	1	8

525

¹⁴⁺8	6	⁶⁺2	¹⁻5	4	¹⁸⁺3	²⁴⁺7	⁷⁻1
¹⁻2	⁷⁻1	4	3	5	7	6	8
1	8	¹⁷⁺3	7	⁸⁺6	5	4	2
²⁰⁺5	¹²⁺7	1	6	2	¹²⁺8	¹⁻3	4
4	5	¹⁻6	¹⁸⁺2	3	1	³¹⁺8	⁷7
7	4	5	1	8	6	2	²⁻3
⁹⁺6	3	8	4	7	¹⁻2	1	5
3	²²⁺2	7	8	1	4	¹¹⁺5	6

526

³⁺2	1	⁷⁻8	¹⁶⁺7	¹⁴⁺6	²⁻5	3	⁶⁺4
²⁷⁺4	7	1	6	8	²⁻3	¹⁻5	2
8	6	2	3	³⁰⁺5	1	4	¹⁸⁺7
¹⁻3	2	6	8	4	7	⁷⁺1	5
²²⁺5	8	¹²⁺7	²⁻1	3	4	2	6
⁸⁺7	4	5	²⁻2	¹⁻1	¹⁴⁺8	¹⁶⁺6	3
1	5	³3	4	2	6	7	⁷⁻8
⁹⁺6	3	¹⁶⁺4	5	7	²2	¹⁰⁺8	1

527

¹⁶⁺8	6	³⁻5	2	⁹⁺3	1	¹¹⁺4	7
2	²⁸⁺8	7	6	4	5	²⁻3	⁴⁺1
⁹⁺4	⁴⁺1	⁸8	7	2	⁴⁻6	5	3
5	3	⁵⁻6	⁴⁻1	³⁶⁺7	2	8	²⁻4
¹⁵⁺3	4	1	5	8	7	6	2
1	5	2	¹¹⁺4	⁷⁺6	³¹⁺3	¹⁵⁺7	8
²⁵⁺6	7	4	3	1	8	2	¹⁻5
7	2	3	8	5	4	1	6

528

²⁻1	²²⁺7	3	²⁰⁺2	5	¹⁻4	¹⁴⁺8	6
3	8	4	6	7	5	⁶⁻1	³⁻2
²⁻6	4	⁴⁺2	1	⁸⁺3	³⁴⁺8	7	5
²⁰⁺8	5	1	3	2	7	¹³⁺6	⁸⁺4
4	3	³⁴⁺7	5	8	6	2	1
¹⁵⁺7	1	8	¹⁶⁺4	6	2	5	3
5	2	6	8	4	²⁻1	⁷⁺3	¹⁵⁺7
⁴⁻2	6	5	⁶⁻7	1	3	4	8

382

529

³15⁺ 3	²⁵⁺ 4	6	5	8	²⁻ 1	7	¹⁶⁺ 2
7	³⁻ 5	8	³²⁺ 4	2	3	6	1
1	3	4	2	6	7	¹⁸⁺ 5	8
4	¹⁷⁺ 7	2	6	¹⁶⁺ 3	8	⁷⁻ 1	5
2	6	⁴⁻ 3	⁶⁻ 7	1	5	8	³⁰⁺ 4
¹⁹⁺ 8	⁷⁻ 1	7	¹⁶⁺ 3	5	4	⁷⁺ 2	6
6	8	⁶⁺ 5	1	4	2	3	7
5	³⁺ 2	1	¹⁵⁺ 8	7	6	4	3

530

¹⁵⁺ 5	6	1	3	⁶⁻ 8	¹⁴⁺ 7	2	4
¹⁷⁺ 7	4	6	¹⁵⁺ 5	2	1	¹⁸⁺ 3	8
¹³⁺ 1	⁸⁺ 3	5	6	4	⁶⁻ 2	8	7
3	5	4	⁵⁻ 7	6	⁴⁴⁺ 8	¹²⁺ 1	³⁺ 2
¹⁷⁺ 8	7	3	2	1	4	¹⁻ 6	¹⁻ 5
2	²⁸⁺ 1	8	4	5	3	7	6
6	8	2	⁷⁻ 1	7	5	¹⁵⁺ 4	⁴⁺ 3
4	2	7	8	³ 3	6	5	1

531

¹²⁺ 2	4	²⁰⁺ 8	6	1	5	¹⁰⁺ 3	7
6	⁴⁻ 1	5	²²⁺ 8	4	3	³⁶⁺ 7	⁸⁺ 2
²⁻ 1	3	⁸⁺ 6	¹⁸⁺ 4	7	8	2	5
⁹⁺ 5	¹¹⁺ 6	2	3	8	7	⁴⁻ 4	1
4	5	⁶⁻ 7	1	3	2	8	²⁻ 6
¹⁰⁺ 3	7	⁸⁺ 1	2	5	4	¹¹⁺ 6	8
²³⁺ 7	8	⁸⁺ 3	5	¹⁶⁺ 2	6	1	4
8	²⁻ 2	4	7	6	1	5	²⁻ 3

532

¹⁴⁺ 2	¹⁶⁺ 4	¹⁷⁺ 6	3	8	¹⁻ 1	¹²⁺ 7	5
8	3	4	5	¹⁸⁺ 7	2	²⁻ 1	⁷⁺ 6
4	⁴⁶⁺ 2	8	7	6	5	3	1
⁴⁻ 1	8	5	²⁻ 2	¹⁰⁺ 3	7	¹⁰⁺ 6	4
5	6	¹³⁺ 1	4	2	3	²³⁺ 8	7
3	7	2	³⁻ 1	4	¹⁻ 6	5	8
²⁻ 7	5	3	¹⁴⁺ 6	¹⁰⁺ 1	¹²⁺ 8	4	⁷⁺ 2
⁷⁺ 6	1	7	8	5	4	2	3

533

2−	4−		20+	10+		5−	
5	8	4	6	1	3	7	2
3	24+ 7	1	5	2	4	12+ 6	14+ 8
7	4	5	3	6	6− 8	2	1
5− 1	6	23+ 7	8	16+ 3	2	4	5
23+ 6	2	8	7	4	4− 1	5	1− 3
8	3	13+ 6	2	26+ 7	5	4+ 1	4
4	5	2	14+ 1	8	6	3	13+ 7
2 2	1	3	4	5	15+ 7	8	6

534

7+		3−		3−	29+	11+	
1	6	3	8	7	4	2	5
3− 4	7	6	5	8	28+ 3	1	2
16+ 5	4	2− 2	5+ 1	6	8	15+ 7	3
7	19+ 2	4	3	1	1− 5	8	6
2	1	7	4	3	6	5	8
25+ 8	9+ 3	1	13+ 6	5	3+ 2	1− 4	12+ 7
6	5	20+ 8	7	2	1	3	4
3	8	5	2− 2	4	13+ 7	6	1

535

2−	22+		19+				9+
5	6	8	4	7	3	2	1
7	14+ 5	6	2	3− 1	4	3	8
2	3	5− 7	32+ 5	8	11+ 1	4	6
21+ 8	4	2	7	6	5	1	9+ 3
6	7	4+ 1	22+ 3	19+ 4	8	19+ 5	2
4+ 1	2	3	6	5	7	8	4
1− 4	1	3− 5	8	3	2	6	25+ 7
3	4− 8	4	1	2	6	7	5

536

25+		10+	43+			4−	
4	7	1	8	5	3	2	6
8	6	3	16+ 7	6− 2	5	3− 4	1
38+ 5	2 2	6	4	8	1	4− 3	7
6	3	4	5	6− 1	2	7	8
6+ 1	5	8	1− 3	7	4	1− 6	2− 2
4− 3	1	7	2	14+ 6	8	5	4
7	4	7+ 2	4+ 1	3	13+ 6	17+ 8	5
6− 2	8	5	10+ 6	4	7	1	3

384

537

5	1	4	8	3	6	2	7
1	2	5	3	8	7	4	6
4	6	2	5	7	8	1	3
3	5	6	2	1	4	7	8
7	8	3	4	6	2	5	1
8	4	7	1	2	3	6	5
6	3	1	7	4	5	8	2
2	7	8	6	5	1	3	4

538

2	6	4	1	3	5	8	7
3	8	2	4	7	1	6	5
5	1	3	2	4	8	7	6
8	3	5	7	1	6	4	2
7	4	6	5	8	2	3	1
1	2	7	8	6	4	5	3
4	7	1	6	5	3	2	8
6	5	8	3	2	7	1	4

539

7	4	2	8	6	3	5	1
8	1	4	2	7	5	3	6
6	5	3	1	2	8	4	7
1	8	6	7	5	4	2	3
5	7	8	3	4	6	1	2
4	3	5	6	1	2	7	8
2	6	1	5	3	7	8	4
3	2	7	4	8	1	6	5

540

3	7	4	5	1	2	8	6
2	1	7	3	8	6	5	4
4	6	8	2	7	1	3	5
7	4	1	8	5	3	6	2
6	8	2	1	3	5	4	7
5	2	3	7	6	4	1	8
8	3	5	6	2	4	7	1
1	5	6	4	2	8	7	3

541

7	5	1	8	2	3	6	4
6	8	3	5	1	4	2	7
2	4	8	6	3	5	7	1
1	6	7	4	5	2	8	3
3	7	5	1	8	6	4	2
8	3	6	2	4	7	1	5
5	2	4	7	6	1	3	8
4	1	2	3	7	8	5	6

542

1	6	2	5	7	4	3	8
6	3	8	7	1	2	5	4
5	1	7	6	8	3	4	2
2	7	3	8	4	6	1	5
4	5	1	2	6	7	8	3
8	2	4	3	5	1	7	6
7	8	6	4	3	5	2	1
3	4	5	1	2	8	6	7

543

4	6	3	5	1	2	7	8
1	5	4	6	8	7	2	3
3	1	5	8	7	4	6	2
8	3	7	2	6	5	4	1
2	7	6	1	5	8	3	4
7	8	2	4	3	1	5	6
5	2	1	3	4	6	8	7
6	4	8	7	2	3	1	5

544

8	7	5	6	1	3	2	4
6	4	1	2	3	7	5	8
1	3	2	4	6	8	7	5
7	8	6	5	4	2	3	1
3	5	4	8	7	6	1	2
5	1	3	7	2	4	8	6
4	2	8	3	5	1	6	7
2	6	7	1	8	5	4	3

545

40×		336×	12×			28×	6÷
8	5	7	1	3	4	2	6
4÷			**105×**				
4	6	8	3	5	2	7	1
	2÷			**2÷**	**144×**		**35×**
1	4	2	7	8	6	3	5
105×	**2÷**	**180×**					
3	2	5	6	4	8	1	7
			56×		**15×**	**4÷**	
5	1	6	4	7	3	8	2
	168×			**2÷**		**120×**	
7	8	3	2	1	5	6	4
36×		**32×**					**3**
6	7	4	8	2	1	5	3
			210×			**2÷**	
2	3	1	5	6	7	4	8

546

168×		80×	2÷		48×	210×	
7	3	4	2	1	8	5	6
	30×			**84×**			**24×**
8	1	5	4	6	2	7	3
20×		**56×**				**8÷**	
5	6	8	7	2	3	1	4
		2÷	**72×**		**252×**		
4	5	1	3	7	6	8	2
	2÷						**40×**
1	4	2	8	3	7	6	5
126×		**336×**			**5**	**2÷**	
3	2	7	6	8	5	4	1
		90×		**4÷**			
6	7	3	5	4	1	2	8
4÷				**5÷**		**84×**	
2	8	6	1	5	4	3	7

547

90×	224×		8	36×	2÷		280×
6	4	7	8	3	1	2	5
					4÷		
3	5	8	6	2	4	1	7
21×			**60×**	**60×**		**192×**	
7	3	1	5	6	2	4	8
2÷					**126×**		
1	2	4	3	5	7	8	6
2÷		**70×**					**2÷**
4	8	5	2	7	6	3	1
4÷	**126×**		**4÷**		**150×**		
8	7	3	1	4	5	6	2
	30×		**56×**		**168×**		**12×**
2	1	6	7	8	3	5	4
		2÷					
5	6	2	4	1	8	7	3

548

2÷	70×			6	105×	8÷	
4	5	7	2	6	3	8	1
	24×	**3÷**				**3÷**	
8	4	2	6	5	7	1	3
		56×		**2÷**	**30×**		**120×**
6	1	8	7	4	2	3	5
42×	**56×**	**30×**			**2÷**		
3	7	6	1	2	8	5	4
				24×		**56×**	
7	8	1	5	3	4	2	6
	36×	**60×**					
2	6	5	3	8	1	4	7
15×				**7÷**	**180×**	**112×**	
5	2	3	4	1	6	7	8
		2÷					
1	3	4	8	7	5	6	2

549

4÷1	4	2÷8	3÷3	3÷2	6	350×5	7
672×7	2	4	1	720×8	3	6	5
120×4	8	6	84×7	3	5	2÷1	2
5	3	24×1	8	4	28×7	2	336×6
2	1	3	30×5	6	4	7	8
108×3	6	140×7	2	280×5	8	4	1
6	5	2	120×4	7	1	8	36×3
56×8	7	5	6	2÷1	2	3	4

550

8×1	2	4	630×6	315×5	7	3	336×8
2÷2	24×4	1	5	3	160×8	7	6
4	1	6	3	7	5	4÷8	2
960×8	5	210×2	7	4	1	126×6	3
1260×6	3	5	2÷8	1	2÷2	2÷4	7
7	8	3	4	2	240×6	5	1
5	6	1176×7	2÷1	576×8	3	2	4
3	7	8	2	6	4	5÷1	5

551

280×7	8	36×3	1	4	240×5	2	3÷6
5	2÷2	4	3	8	6	1	294×7
280×2	4	7	5	540×6	1	8	8÷3
2÷4	5÷5	1	6	3	336×8	7	2
8	168×3	2	4	5	7	6	1
3÷1	1440×6	5	7	84×2	4	3	480×8
3	336×1	6	8	7	2	80×4	5
6	7	8	2÷2	1	3	5	4

552

288×8	3	4	1260×6	5	7	12×1	2÷2
3	40×5	8	280×7	2	4÷6	4	1
60×6	2	5	4	8	1	3	630×7
1	8×8	882×7	5	2÷4	2	6	3
2÷4	1	3	48×2	6	8	280×7	5
2	7	6	3÷1	3	5	8	360×4
210×7	2÷4	2	168×8	1	3	5	6
5	6	1	3	7	64×4	2	8

388

553

2÷ 1	96× 6	2	8	112× 7	4	630× 3	5
2	315× 5	3	4	1	48× 8	7	6
160× 5	4÷ 2	7	3	6	1	280× 4	672× 8
4	8	120× 6	1	5	7	2	3
8	3÷ 3	1	5	4	216× 2	6	7
168× 6	8÷ 1	8	336× 7	2	3	200× 5	4
7	4	420× 5	3÷ 2	3	6	8	2÷ 1
3	7	4	6	8	5	1	2

554

480× 5	420× 2	7	6	192× 4	8	1	168× 3
3	4	8	5	6	2	7	1
840× 6	5	48× 3	2	1	5÷ 4	8	7
7÷ 1	7	4	8	5	3	480× 2	6
7	6÷ 6	1	2÷ 4	2	5× 5	360× 3	8
2÷ 4	720× 3	112× 2	7	8	1	6	5
2	8	6	1	63× 3	336× 7	5	4
8÷ 8	1	5	3	7	6	4	2

555

140× 5	7	4	280× 1	8	2	216× 6	3
24× 4	1	4÷ 2	8	7	5	120× 3	6
42× 3	6	504× 7	2÷ 2	4	1	8	5
1	2÷ 4	6	3	5÷ 5	896× 8	2	7
7	2	72× 3	4	1	1260× 6	5	8
2	3	8	1400× 5	6	7	4÷ 1	4
240× 6	8	5	7	168× 2	3	4	2÷ 1
8	5	1	72× 6	3	4	7	2

556

2÷ 2	56× 4	504× 6	168× 7	8	3	120× 5	1
1	2	7	2÷ 4	240× 6	8	3	240× 5
480× 5	7	3	2	4	6	1	8
3	8	4	6÷ 1	2	5	126× 7	6
4	840× 5	8	6	7÷ 7	1	3÷ 2	3
7	3	150× 5	8÷ 8	1	56× 2	6	2÷ 4
96× 8	6	1	45× 5	3	7	4	2
6	1	2	3	5	224× 4	8	7

557

^{2940×}7	6	2	^{3÷}1	3	^{160×}5	^{2÷}8	4
5	1	7	^{3÷}6	2	8	4	^{3×}3
^{4÷}2	8	^{60×}4	3	^{210×}5	7	6	1
^{2÷}6	3	5	^{128×}8	4	^{42×}1	^{70×}7	2
^{24×}8	^{2÷}2	1	4	7	6	^{48×}3	5
3	^{40320×}5	6	7	1	^{72×}4	2	8
1	4	8	2	6	3	^{210×}5	7
^{28×}4	7	3	^{40×}5	8	^{2÷}2	1	6

558

^{3÷}2	6	^{98×}7	^{160×}5	8	4	^{72×}3	^{5÷}1
^{28×}4	7	2	^{30×}6	1	3	8	5
7	1	^{120×}6	4	5	^{12544×}8	2	^{24×}3
^{2÷}6	3	5	^{2÷}2	4	7	1	8
^{40×}5	^{86016×}2	8	1	^{2÷}3	6	4	7
8	4	1	3	7	^{5÷}5	^{72×}6	2
^{30240×}3	5	4	8	2	1	^{140×}7	6
1	8	3	7	6	2	5	4

559

^{56×}7	8	^{48×}3	4	^{48×}2	^{25200×}6	1	5
^{1260×}2	1	4	^{2÷}3	6	7	5	8
5	7	1	6	4	3	^{160×}8	^{2÷}2
6	3	^{840×}7	^{320×}8	5	1	2	4
^{8÷}1	4	6	5	8	2	^{16128×}7	3
8	^{12×}6	2	^{42×}7	3	5	4	^{7÷}1
^{120×}3	5	8	2	^{35×}1	4	6	7
^{2÷}4	2	5	1	7	8	^{2÷}3	6

560

^{24×}3	2	4	^{112×}8	7	^{88200×}6	^{7÷}1	^{5÷}5
^{2÷}6	3	8	4	2	5	7	1
^{48×}8	1	^{60×}2	6	5	3	4	7
^{1960×}2	6	^{17280×}1	3	^{8×}4	7	5	^{2÷}8
5	7	6	2	1	^{4÷}8	^{54×}3	4
7	4	5	1	8	2	6	3
4	^{15×}5	3	^{1960×}7	6	^{96×}1	8	2
1	8	7	5	^{24×}3	4	2	6

561

8 [15120×]	3	6	7	4 [320×]	2	5	1 [7÷]
4 [56×]	2	1 [24×]	5	8	3 [2÷]	6	7
7	6	4	3	2 [2÷]	1	8 [120×]	5
6 [12×]	1	2	8 [9216×]	5 [15×]	7 [28×]	4	3
1 [10×]	5	8	4	3	6 [126×]	7	2 [2÷]
2	7 [280×]	5	6	1 [8×]	8	3	4
5 [60×]	8	3	2	7 [210×]	4 [24×]	1	6
3	4	7 [7÷]	1	6	5	2 [4÷]	8

562

3 [3÷]	2 [4÷]	8	5 [210×]	7 [2240×]	6 [24×]	4	1
1	6 [210×]	7	3	8	5	2	4
5	7	2	6 [40320×]	1	4 [2÷]	8	3 [105×]
4 [4÷]	1	3 [45×]	8	6 [3÷]	2	7	5
8 [448×]	3	5	1	4	7	6	2 [16128×]
7	8	4 [2÷]	2	5 [45×]	3	1	6
2 [10080×]	4	6	7	3	1	5	8
6	5	1 [8×]	4	2	8	3	7

563

8 [24×]	1	2 [3÷]	6	5 [30×]	4 [28×]	7 [168×]	3
2 [24×]	3	7 [280×]	5 [40×]	6	1	8	4 [1680×]
3	4	5	8	1	7	6 [3÷]	2
1 [42×]	6	8	4 [4÷]	3 [120×]	5	2	7
7	2 [2÷]	4	1	8	3 [720×]	5	6
4 [120×]	7 [280×]	6 [18×]	3	2	8	1	5
5	8	3	2 [14×]	7 [168×]	6	4	1
6	5	1	7	4 [2÷]	2	3 [24×]	8

564

1 [768×]	2 [23040×]	6	4	8	5	7 [105×]	3 [105×]
2	8	4	6 [48×]	1	3	5	7
4	6 [1890×]	3	8	2	7 [112×]	1	5
7 [35×]	3	5	1	6	8	4 [2÷]	2
5	4 [168×]	1	7	3 [15×]	2	6 [288×]	8 [8÷]
6	7	8 [280×]	3	5	4	2	1
8 [24×]	5	7	2 [2÷]	4	1	3 [2÷]	6
3	1	2 [70×]	5	7	6	8 [2÷]	4

565

⁴⁴⁸ˣ 7	8	¹²ˣ 2	6	¹⁶ˣ 4	²²⁵ˣ 3	5	1
8	³÷ 2	⁵⁰⁴⁰ˣ 7	4	1	⁴²ˣ 6	3	5
²÷ 2	6	5	8	⁴²⁰⁰⁰ˣ 3	7	1	³²ˣ 4
1	¹³⁴⁴⁰ˣ 4	6	3	³÷ 5	2	⁵⁶ˣ 7	8
5	7	3	1	8	4	⁸⁴ˣ 2	6
4	3	8	5	2	⁴⁸ˣ 1	6	7
²÷ 6	⁸ˣ 1	4	2	7	5	8	²⁴ˣ 3
3	³⁵ˣ 5	1	7	⁴⁸ˣ 6	8	4	2

566

¹⁶ˣ 1	4	³³⁶ˣ 6	³⁰ˣ 5	3	7	³⁰²⁴⁰ˣ 8	2
4	7	8	2	⁵ˣ 1	5	3	6
⁸⁴ˣ 6	2	³⁹⁶⁹⁰ˣ 7	1	¹⁶⁰ˣ 4	8	5	3
7	¹⁶ˣ 1	3	6	5	²÷ 2	²÷ 4	8
⁴⁰ˣ 5	8	2	3	⁸⁴ˣ 7	4	²⁴ˣ 6	1
8	3	5	7	2	6	²÷ 1	4
³⁰ˣ 3	5	²÷ 4	8	⁶ˣ 6	1	2	²⁴⁵ˣ 7
2	⁶÷ 6	1	⁹⁶ˣ 4	8	3	7	5

567

⁴⁶⁰⁸⁰ˣ 4	6	5	8	2	⁷ˣ 1	7	⁸⁴ˣ 3
³⁰ˣ 5	2	¹⁶ˣ 8	6	³¹⁵⁰ˣ 3	7	1	²⁴ˣ 4
3	8	7	5	1	¹⁹²ˣ 6	4	²÷ 2
2	5	3	⁷÷ 7	4	8	6	1
⁸⁰⁶⁴ˣ 8	7	2	1	⁴⁰ˣ 5	4	²÷ 3	6
⁵⁶ˣ 1	4	6	3	³³⁶ˣ 8	2	⁹⁶⁰⁰ˣ 5	³⁵ˣ 7
7	1	4	2	6	3	8	5
²÷ 6	3	⁴÷ 1	4	7	5	2	8

568

⁵⁰⁴⁰⁰ˣ 4	1	3	²⁴⁰ˣ 6	8	5	⁹⁴⁰⁸ˣ 2	7
⁴⁸ˣ 1	6	7	4	3	2	5	8
¹²⁰ˣ 6	8	5	²⁴ˣ 1	²÷ 2	3	7	4
5	4	²÷ 2	8	1	³³⁶ˣ 7	⁹⁰ˣ 3	6
¹¹²ˣ 2	7	4	3	6	8	¹³⁸²⁴ˣ 1	5
8	³÷ 2	6	²⁴⁵ˣ 7	5	1	4	3
⁶³ˣ 3	⁸⁰ˣ 5	8	2	7	4	6	²÷ 1
7	3	1	²⁰ˣ 5	4	6	8	2

569

^{16128×}4	8	^{1260×}7	2	5	3	^{6÷}6	1
2	^{2÷}3	^{120×}8	1	6	^{7÷}7	^{40×}5	^{56×}4
7	6	3	^{120×}5	4	1	8	2
3	2	5	6	^{7÷}1	^{128×}8	4	7
1	^{90×}5	6	3	7	4	^{48×}2	8
6	^{14×}7	2	^{192×}4	^{40×}8	5	^{7÷}1	3
^{40×}5	^{16×}4	1	8	3	2	7	^{7560×}6
8	1	4	7	2	6	3	5

570

^{1344×}7	6	^{16×}2	8	^{30×}5	^{21×}3	^{6÷}1	^{40×}4
8	^{12×}4	1	3	2	7	6	5
1	3	^{210×}6	5	7	^{2÷}4	8	2
4	1	^{47040×}5	7	3	^{96×}6	2	8
^{50×}5	2	7	4	8	1	^{126×}3	6
2	5	^{2÷}3	6	1	^{240×}8	^{28×}4	7
^{2÷}3	^{2÷}8	4	^{112×}2	6	5	7	1
6	7	8	1	^{2÷}4	2	^{15×}5	3

571

^{80×}8	5	^{16×}4	¹³⁺1	⁴⁻7	3	^{3÷}6	2
2	4	1	7	5	⁸8	³⁻3	6
^{7÷}1	^{40×}8	5	⁵⁻3	^{3÷}2	6	¹¹⁺7	4
7	^{54×}6	3	8	⁷⁺1	^{2÷}4	2	^{40×}5
⁵5	3	³⁻7	4	6	¹⁻2	1	8
¹⁴⁺4	2	8	¹³⁺6	3	1	²⁻5	7
¹⁰⁺6	1	³⁻2	5	4	²⁰⁺7	^{2÷}8	²⁻3
3	¹⁵⁺7	6	2	8	5	4	1

572

^{3÷}6	^{4÷}1	²⁻7	5	¹²⁺3	8	^{2÷}4	2
2	4	¹⁻6	7	⁴⁻8	1	⁸⁺3	5
^{448×}7	8	¹⁻2	3	4	¹²⁺5	6	1
8	^{28×}7	1	4	¹⁸⁺5	6	^{24×}2	3
^{30×}3	5	^{2÷}8	2	6	7	¹²⁺1	4
⁴⁻5	2	4	^{6÷}1	^{14×}7	3	8	⁶6
1	¹³⁺3	¹⁶⁺5	6	2	²⁻4	¹²⁺7	¹⁻8
4	6	3	8	1	2	5	7

573

42× 3	2	7	5 5	4	10+ 6	8	7÷ 1
9+ 1	4	112× 8	2	6	12+ 3	14+ 5	7
4	3− 5	2	7	8	1	3	2− 6
3− 5	63× 3	4÷ 1	4	7	5− 2	6	8
8	7	3	6÷ 6	1	4− 4	5− 2	2− 5
15+ 2	144× 6	4	5÷ 1	5	8	7	3
7	9+ 1	6	8	16+ 3	10+ 5	4	2÷ 2
6	8	5	3	2	28× 7	1	4

574

5÷ 5	6− 8	2	4− 7	6	15+ 4	4÷ 1	15+ 3
1	17+ 6	5	3	2	7	8	4
12+ 3	3− 7	6	14+ 8	2÷ 4	50× 2	5	6× 1
7	4	24× 1	6	8	5	3	2
2	3	8	5÷ 5	35× 7	1	192× 4	6
2− 6	2÷ 2	4	1	5	4− 3	7	8
8	10+ 5	4− 3	9+ 4	1	8+ 6	2	2− 7
4	1	7	2	3	2− 8	6	5

575

20× 5	12+ 2	6	4	3÷ 1	15+ 7	3	17+ 8
4	7÷ 7	1	10+ 6	3	5	192× 8	2
3− 2	5	3	1	96× 8	6	4	7
21× 1	8 8	2− 4	15+ 7	2	1− 3	150× 6	5
7	3	2	8	6	4	5	6÷ 1
1− 3	4	3− 5	2	15+ 7	16+ 8	1	6
2− 6	8÷ 1	8	3	5	2÷ 2	7	9+ 4
8	6	1− 7	5	1− 4	1	2	3

576

11+ 1	4	3− 6	3	1− 2	15+ 7	3− 8	5
6	112× 7	2	20+ 5	3	8	4÷ 4	1
2− 4	2÷ 2	8	7	2− 1	3	18+ 5	6
2	1	3 3	8	1− 6	5	7	64× 4
15+ 7	3	12+ 1	6	5	14+ 4	1− 2	8
5	144× 8	2− 7	4÷ 1	4	6	3	2
3	6	5	4	112× 8	2	7+ 1	7
3− 8	5	2÷ 4	2	10+ 7	1	6	3

577

13+		8+	5−	17+			48×
1	6	5	3	7	2	8	4
6	1	2	8	5	7	4	3
5	7	1	4	6	8	3	2
2	8	7	5	4	3	6	1
8	5	6	2	3	4	1	7
7	3	4	6	2	1	5	8
3	4	8	7	1	5	2	6
4	2	3	1	8	6	7	5

578

6	2	1	4	8	7	5	3
1	3	5	7	6	8	4	2
4	7	2	8	1	5	3	6
2	5	4	6	7	3	8	1
5	4	8	2	3	6	1	7
7	6	3	5	4	1	2	8
8	1	7	3	5	2	6	4
3	8	6	1	2	4	7	5

579

7	1	4	6	8	2	3	5
2	7	8	5	6	4	1	3
4	5	6	3	2	1	8	7
1	3	2	4	7	6	5	8
8	2	5	1	3	7	4	6
3	4	7	8	1	5	6	2
6	8	1	7	5	3	2	4
5	6	3	2	4	8	7	1

580

1	3	7	6	4	8	2	5
3	6	5	4	1	2	8	7
7	5	6	1	2	4	3	8
2	8	3	7	5	1	6	4
4	1	2	8	7	6	5	3
8	7	5	1	6	3	4	2
6	2	4	3	8	5	7	1
5	4	8	2	3	7	1	6

581

6	1	7	3	4	8	2	5
1	8	2	7	5	4	6	3
2	4	5	8	3	7	1	6
5	2	6	4	8	1	3	7
4	7	3	1	2	6	5	8
8	5	4	6	1	3	7	2
3	6	8	2	7	5	4	1
7	3	1	5	6	2	8	4

582

8	7	3	4	1	6	2	5
5	3	8	1	7	2	6	4
4	8	1	6	5	7	3	2
7	4	5	2	8	3	1	6
6	5	2	7	3	8	4	1
2	1	4	3	6	5	7	8
1	6	7	8	2	4	5	3
3	2	6	5	4	1	8	7

583

4	5	8	3	1	6	2	7
2	3	5	6	7	4	8	1
6	8	4	1	2	7	3	5
3	7	1	4	8	2	5	6
7	6	2	8	5	1	4	3
5	1	6	2	4	3	7	8
1	4	7	5	3	8	6	2
8	2	3	7	6	5	1	4

584

2	3	5	4	7	6	1	8
1	5	4	8	3	2	7	6
3	6	8	5	2	7	4	1
8	2	7	1	4	3	6	5
5	7	3	2	6	1	8	4
4	1	6	7	8	5	2	3
7	8	1	6	5	4	3	2
6	4	2	3	1	8	5	7

585

1	8	3	5	4	6	7	2
7	1	2	4	5	3	8	6
2	5	6	7	3	1	4	8
3	6	7	8	2	4	5	1
4	2	1	3	7	8	6	5
6	3	4	2	8	5	1	7
8	4	5	6	1	7	2	3
5	7	8	1	6	2	3	4

Cage clues: 7−, 2−, 15+, 25+, 4−, 8+, 2−, 11+, 25+, 64×, 8÷, 23+, 768×, 1−, 11+, 320×, 160×, 3÷, 1−, 7÷, 12+, 2−, 6÷

586

5	2	6	1	3	7	8	4
7	4	5	2	8	6	1	3
4	1	3	8	5	2	7	6
3	5	8	4	7	1	6	2
1	3	4	7	6	8	2	5
2	6	7	3	1	5	4	8
8	7	2	6	4	3	5	1
6	8	1	5	2	4	3	7

Cage clues: 13+, 42×, 2÷, 14+, 1−, 3−, 4−, 4+, 120×, 336×, 21+, 1568×, 2÷, 252×, 6÷, 2−, 13+, 360×, 2−, 11+, 5÷, 40×, 4−

587

4	5	7	2	3	1	6	8
8	4	1	3	6	2	7	5
2	3	4	5	7	8	1	6
1	6	2	8	5	3	4	7
6	8	5	7	1	4	2	3
5	7	8	1	2	6	3	4
3	1	6	4	8	7	5	2
7	2	3	6	4	5	8	1

Cage clues: 2÷, 2−, 18×, 6÷, 280×, 27+, 240×, 1−, 126×, 6÷, 4480×, 2÷, 14+, 14×, 72×, 2−, 1, 2−, 96×, 280×, 42×, 14+

588

5	2	8	6	1	7	4	3
7	8	2	4	3	1	5	6
3	5	6	1	2	4	7	8
2	4	1	8	6	5	3	7
1	6	3	5	7	2	8	4
4	1	7	3	8	6	2	5
6	3	4	7	5	8	1	2
8	7	5	2	4	3	6	1

Cage clues: 15+, 128×, 14, 2880×, 48×, 3÷, 40×, 2÷, 28×, 4320×, 8820×, 4×, 33+, 196×, 5−, 2÷, 1−, 280×, 2−, 2÷

589

⁵⁶ˣ 2	⁵⁻ 3	¹⁵⁺ 1	8	²⁴⁵ˣ 7	5	²⁻ 6	4
4	8	6	⁴ˣ 2	1	7	⁴⁸⁰ˣ 5	3
7	²²⁺ 6	³⁵ˣ 5	¹¹⁺ 3	2	4	8	⁸÷ 1
6	4	7	5	3	² 2	²⁷⁺ 1	8
1	¹³⁺ 5	8	²⁴⁺ 7	4	3	2	6
5	²÷ 1	2	4	6	8	3	²⁹⁴⁰ˣ 7
⁵⁻ 3	2	4	1	²⁴⁰ˣ 8	6	7	5
8	²¹ˣ 7	3	6	5	⁴÷ 1	4	2

590

²÷ 8	4	¹⁻ 7	6	⁷⁵⁶⁰ˣ 3	2	³⁻ 5	1
³÷ 2	⁴⁸ˣ 8	6	7	5	3	¹⁴ˣ 1	4
6	⁵÷ 5	1	3	8	¹¹⁺ 4	2	7
²⁵²⁰ˣ 3	6	5	²⁸ˣ 4	7	1	¹²⁸ˣ 8	2
³⁵ˣ 5	7	4	¹⁶ˣ 1	⁴⁻ 2	6	¹²⁺ 3	8
7	⁷⁺ 1	2	8	6	5	4	¹²⁶ˣ 3
4	2	⁵⁻ 3	¹⁴⁺ 5	1	8	7	6
²⁻ 1	3	8	²÷ 2	4	¹⁸⁺ 7	6	5

591

²⁴ˣ 6	1	³⁷⁸⁰⁰ˣ 3	7	³³⁺ 8	2	5	4
4	¹⁻ 2	1	5	⁴⁻ 3	7	6	8
⁴÷ 8	4	5	3	6	¹⁴ˣ 1	7	2
2	¹²⁶ˣ 3	¹⁻ 7	6	⁴⁻ 1	⁹²¹⁶⁰ˣ 4	8	³⁰ˣ 5
⁴⁻ 1	7	6	⁴ˣ 4	5	8	2	3
5	¹²⁸ˣ 8	2	1	4	6	3	⁷ˣ 7
²÷ 3	6	8	2	¹⁴ˣ 7	5	⁴ 4	1
¹²⁺ 7	5	²÷ 4	8	⁵⁺ 2	3	⁶÷ 1	6

592

⁴÷ 1	³⁻ 5	8	⁹⁰⁷²⁰ˣ 7	2	4	3	6
4	⁴÷ 8	2	6	¹⁴⁺ 7	5	³ˣ 1	3
¹⁶ˣ 8	²⁰⁺ 4	¹²⁺ 6	5	3	2	⁶⁻ 7	1
2	3	5	¹²⁸ˣ 8	¹¹⁺ 1	7	²⁻ 6	4
7	6	1	2	8	3	¹²⁺ 4	¹⁰ˣ 5
²⁻ 5	7	¹²⁺ 4	¹⁸⁺ 3	6	⁶÷ 1	8	2
²÷ 3	1	7	³⁸⁴⁰ˣ 4	5	6	²²⁺ 2	8
6	2	3	1	4	8	5	7

593

¹⁵⁺1	6	8	⁸ˣ4	2	¹⁰ˣ5	²⁶⁺3	7
⁷⁵ˣ5	3	⁶⁻7	1	³⁶ˣ6	2	²⁰⁺8	4
³⁻7	5	1	2	3	8	4	6
4	²÷2	²⁶ˣ6	7	8	⁴⁰³²ˣ3	5	1
³÷6	1	¹⁻2	3	5	4	7	8
2	³⁵ˣ7	5	⁹⁴⁰⁸ˣ8	4	6	⁶÷1	3
³3	¹⁵⁺8	4	¹⁻5	1	7	6	2
²÷8	4	3	6	7	¹⁰ˣ1	2	5

594

²ˣ1	2	¹⁻3	³⁵ˣ5	7	¹⁴⁰ˣ4	²⁻8	6
¹⁰ˣ2	1	4	³³⁶ˣ6	5	7	⁴⁴¹⁰⁰ˣ3	²÷8
5	³⁷⁺3	7	8	⁴⁸ˣ2	6	1	4
6	4	5	3	8	1	7	2
4	⁷⁰⁵⁶ˣ6	8	1	3	2	5	7
8	7	¹⁰⁺1	2	²÷6	3	²⁻4	5
3	⁸8	²⁴⁰ˣ6	7	⁴÷4	²⁴⁰ˣ5	2	³÷1
7	5	2	4	1	8	6	3

595

⁶6	⁵⁶ˣ7	8	1	¹⁸⁰⁰⁰ˣ5	3	²⁷⁺2	²4
²⁴¹⁹²ˣ3	6	4	5	1	7	8	2
7	3	5	8	6	²÷2	4	³⁵ˣ1
2	1	³³⁶ˣ7	3	8	4	6	5
³⁻4	8	⁶÷1	6	2	³⁰ˣ5	³⁸⁺3	7
1	⁴⁰⁰ˣ5	2	4	3	6	7	⁵⁻8
5	2	¹⁸ˣ6	⁹⁸ˣ7	4	8	1	3
²÷8	4	3	2	7	1	5	6

596

¹⁶⁺2	6	8	⁷⁰⁵⁶⁰ˣ4	5	7	1	²⁴ˣ3
1	7	3	6	³³⁺2	4	¹⁵⁰ˣ5	8
²⁴⁺4	1	¹⁴ˣ7	8	3	5	6	¹⁰⁺2
5	3	1	2	6	²÷8	4	7
6	4	⁵⁰ˣ2	5	7	²⁰¹⁶⁰ˣ3	8	1
¹⁻8	2	5	⁸⁺3	1	6	7	4
7	³⁻5	4	1	²÷8	²÷2	⁶ˣ3	6
³3	8	¹⁻6	7	4	1	2	5

399

597

6	3	7	1	8	5	4	2
3	4	6	5	1	2	8	7
7	1	4	8	2	6	5	3
5	6	1	4	3	7	2	8
2	7	3	6	5	8	1	4
4	8	5	2	7	3	6	1
1	2	8	3	6	4	7	5
8	5	2	7	4	1	3	6

598

8	3	2	6	7	1	4	5
3	6	8	2	1	7	5	4
4	7	3	8	6	5	1	2
6	1	4	7	5	3	2	8
2	5	1	4	3	8	6	7
7	4	5	3	2	6	8	1
1	2	7	5	8	4	3	6
5	8	6	1	4	2	7	3

599

4	1	6	3	8	2	5	7
2	7	5	8	6	4	3	1
6	3	8	4	2	7	1	5
8	5	7	6	1	3	4	2
3	8	2	1	4	5	7	6
5	6	4	2	7	1	8	3
1	4	3	7	5	6	2	8
7	2	1	5	3	8	6	4

600

7	8	2	4	5	3	1	6
4	6	7	8	1	2	3	5
6	2	8	1	7	5	4	3
2	3	5	6	4	7	8	1
8	7	6	2	3	1	5	4
1	5	3	7	2	4	6	8
5	1	4	3	6	8	7	2
3	4	1	5	8	6	2	7